E. PAVLIK · B. MACHEI

A Combined Control System for the Process Industries

A Combined Control System
for the Process Industries

Principle, Components and Instruments

of the TELEPERM-TELEPNEU System

By ERNST PAVLIK AND BRUNO MACHEI

Development Department
Siemens & Halske Aktiengesellschaft
Wernerwerk für Messtechnik

With 150 Illustrations and Tables

D. VAN NOSTRAND COMPANY, INC.
PRINCETON, NEW JERSEY
TORONTO · NEW YORK · LONDON

Title of German original edition:

EIN KOMBINIERTES REGELSYSTEM FÜR
DIE VERFAHRENSINDUSTRIE

Translated from German by David J. Fraade, Hans Georg Haeseler and Olaf Kübler

Published by R. Oldenbourg, München

D. VAN NOSTRAND COMPANY, INC.

120 Alexander St., Princeton, New Jersey (*Principal office*)

D. VAN NOSTRAND COMPANY, LTD.

358 Kensington High Street, London, W. 14, England

D. VAN NOSTRAND COMPANY (Canada), LTD.

25 Hollinger Road, Toronto 16, Canada

TABLE OF CONTENTS

8

PREFACE

Standardized control systems are gaining increasing importance in the automatic control of large industrial processing plants. Their special advantages, compared to single instrument construction, are based on the fact that the process variables to be controlled are converted by transmitters into standardized signals. Thus, it has been possible to design modular electric and pneumatic control systems. Since the pneumatic actuation of final control elements offers special advantages, the electric solution mandates transducing from electric to pneumatic. In principle, it is of no consequence where in the control loop transducing is performed. In the TELEPERM-TELEPNEU System, for the first time, all possibilities of transducing are embodied. Similar instrumentation of control rooms for both kinds of control permits random combination and provides the optimum technical and economical solution of the most diverse problems encountered in industrial processing plants.

The many features of this comprehensive electropneumatic control system can only be utilized to a maximum if the design of the individual instruments, their compatibility and the fields of application of the different combinations are well known. It is the aim of this book to give all details required for this purpose. It has been mainly prepared as a reference for the design engineer who is familiar with the fundamentals of control technology. Furthermore, it will be a valuable aid for engineers concerned with maintenance and servicing both in the field and in the shop.

The present book does not give a complete description of the combined system. Rather, it is limited to the pneumatic and electropneumatic components. The electric components will be dealt with in a separate book. Further, transmitters are not treated here as they are the input components and do not affect the combined system proper.

The development of an extended line of instruments can only be done with team work. The TELEPERM-TELEPNEU System, too, is the result of such cooperation between a large number of people. The authors herewith acknowledge the kind help and cooperation of their following colleagues: O. Bauersachs, K. F. Früh, W. Heinrich, W. Schütze, and G. Weidemann. Special credit is due to Mrs. H. Steinbach for her efforts in preparing the illustrations. It is a pleasure to express our indebtness to Dr. L. Merz, Professor of Measuring and Control Technology, for his help and assistance in the preparation of this book.

Karlsruhe, December 1959

H. SARTORIUS

I. AUTOMATION IN THE PROCESS INDUSTRIES

When speaking of automation in the process industries, the most common application is in large petroleum refineries or chemical plants. In fact, industrial automation was first developed in this field. Even in this realm, however, the stage of development is not yet finished. In the last few years, processing was further improved and refined in order to realize a maximum quality yield, together with a minimum of energy. This striving today for an optimum of efficiency is characteristic for all plants in the process industries; steel, drugs, food, power plants, etc. Naturally, this goal can only be obtained by the increased use of controlling elements of which, sometimes, quite new features are required. Therefore, controlling elements have to be available which fulfill today's operational and technical requirements.

A. Scope and Requirements

1. INSTRUMENTATION OF PLANTS IN THE PROCESS INDUSTRIES

The instrumentation of a modern plant in the realm of the process industries is carried out in the following manner:
All operating variables which could possibly have any effect on production are handled by transmitters which convert them into standardized transfer variables. These variables may be of the electric (current, voltage) or of the pneumatic kind. In a central control room, they are continuously monitored by indicating and recording devices. If desired, they are maintained at a constant level by automatic controllers. The number of automatic control operations is steadily on the increase.
Where some years ago a manual control valve would have been sufficient to control the flow, today a locally mounted flow controller is

usually applied. The valve is not regulated directly any more, but is a function of the set point of the flow controller. By these means, a much more accurate flow is obtained and the total effect of the many individual control operations involved in a plant is to eliminate all disturbances and their corresponding effects on the process. The process then continues on such an even basis that no difficulties exist in keeping the operating variables within the closest

Fig. 1   Instrumentation with TELEPERM-TELEPNEU Units in the Central Control Room of a Process Plant.

possible limits to give the optimum in economic operation. The aim of automation mentioned in the beginning—namely, to obtain an optimum of economy—always requires a considerable amount of control loops.

The process is controlled from a central room (Fig. 1) by means of instrument set points for parameters whose desired values determine the quality of the product. Today, this is still largely done by operating personnel, but the last step of complete automation (closed loop) is already here. The automatic monitoring and control of product quality would be done by stream analysis instruments. In recent times, so-called data handling systems are employed in increasing number. They convert the measured variables or output variables of the specific transmitters digitally, store them, print them, count them, and record them on punch cards or evaluate them in another manner for computing purposes. Thus, the plant operators are relieved of painstaking routine operations and the time for material balances is so shortened that daily interim balances may be available if so required.

This system of controlling instrumentation is supplemented by many safety and alarm signal devices which monitor the numerous instruments.

On the whole, instrumentation in an automated processing plant is quite complicated. Trouble-free production always depends on a very large number of control devices. Therefore, special require-ments are necessary as to their operational and technical characteristics.

2. Operational and Technical Requirements

a) Dependability

In every case the most important requirement is dependability. Since there is no absolute precaution against malfunctioning, there must be at least the possibility to quickly replace defective parts without adjustments or interruption of plant operations.

b) Dimensions of the Instruments

The installation of a large number of indicating and recording instruments in control rooms mandates that their size be kept as small as possible. All instruments not directly required by the operators for process control, e. g., the controllers, are either mounted behind the panel boards or in the plants, e. g., locally out in the yard as shown in Fig. 2. In this way coordination is increased and process control is made easier.

c) Economy

Aside from the purely operational requirements, economic aspects play an important part, too; investments in capital expenditures are very important when instruments are used in quantity. This re-

quires that instrument prices must be justifiable, service and maintenance costs have to be low, and warehousing of spare parts shall be
as economical as possible. To the costs of the instruments must be
added the costs of their installation. Furthermore, the operating
costs must also be considered, which, however, will be only sig-
nificant where pneumatic systems are employed.

Fig. 2   Pneumatic Controllers Mounted on the Valves in a Chemical Plant.

d) Accuracy

The requirements of the instrument functions are rather high and
are not always easily brought into harmony with the desired operating requirements. Thus, the permissible error within normal
operating conditions is considerably below the 1% limit. This may
seem to be exaggerated for rugged plant instruments. Since the
errors from the sensing, transmission, and amplification are ac-
cumulative in automatic control, the stress on this accuracy requirement becomes understandable.

e) Compatibility

The types of instruments are influenced mostly by the demand on simple and large-style compatibility. It is required that systems involving cascade and ratio control, disturbance feed forward systems, etc. (which are sometimes quite complicated) can easily be set up without necessitating long calibration and field adjusting work. Naturally, this can only be accomplished by a complete and well-balanced equipment program, not by individual special instruments.

B. The Choice of the Control System

Until recently, the control of petroleum refineries and chemical processing plants was solely through pneumatics. In recent years, however, remarkable advances in electronic control occurred for all fields being automated and it seemed that electronic control was going to completely replace pneumatics. This prediction has not been confirmed, however. Pneumatic control has maintained its place not only in the hazardous atmospheres found in the petroleum and chemical industries but, on the whole, in all operations. The reason for this is that both electronic and pneumatic control have specific advantages which make them the best technical solution for certain specific requirements. There will still be plants where electronic control is indicated and ones where pneumatic control is preferred. Naturally, one must not overlook the fact that both systems have restrictions limiting their fields of application. It will become more and more necessary to combine both systems in order to combine their mutual advantages, to avoid the disadvantages and, thereby, to always arrive at the most reasonable technical solution.

1. Pneumatic Control

Pneumatic control has undergone a rapid development in the past decade. Instrument designs were improved, their construction standardized and special devices were abandoned in favor of integrated families of instruments. The instruments have achieved a precision and accuracy to satisfy even the severest operating requirements. Excellent components are available as the metal bellows, torsion restrictions, and flapper-nozzle systems. By use of such parts, amplifier elements and time derivative elements are so easily constructed that pneumatic controlling instruments are as attractive as electronic instruments, notwithstanding their dependability and prices, too.

A special feature of pneumatic control is the diaphragm motor by which considerable forces at high positioning speeds may be realized. This feature makes pneumatic control particularly suitable for fast acting processes. This is probably the main reason for using pneumatic control in the very important application of fluid flow control. Pneumatic control always gives excellent results, especially when the controllers are locally mounted on the diaphragm valve motors. Here are the advantages of pneumatics in a nutshell:

> High dependability,
> Inherent explosion-proofing,
> High accuracy,
> Great positioning speed.

The limitations of pneumatics are inherent in the transmission distances involved. Because of the limited transmission velocity of pressures in the range of about 300 m/sec, the dead time is of considerable importance where long control loop impulse lines are used and always has a negative effect on the control loop. This downgrading of control system dynamics is heightened where the process is quicker acting. This affects flow control to a much greater degree than temperature control systems where the effect is scarcely noticable. By mounting the controller locally in the plant, instead of mounting it in the control room, this difficulty may be eliminated. In fact, widespread use is made of this possibility in the field of flow control. Therefore, it is difficult to fix upon an exact range of applicability in pneumatic systems. Practically, it can only be limited in the largest of plants, such as petroleum refineries. Operational advantages can be realized only when the whole refinery is controlled from a single control room instead of from several individual ones and when this control room is located outside of the hazardous area. Here, distances of several 1000 meters may occur between the control room and the remotest parts of the plant, and the resulting difficulties can be overcome only with electrical systems.

2. ELECTRIC CONTROL

The advantages of electric control compared with pneumatic control are clear in the process measurement aspects. The more complicated processes demand more complicated measuring and computing systems. We need here only to consider the square root extraction of differential pressures, the correction of gaseous flows to normal conditions, and the addition of several measured values. These are all tasks which can be very comprehensively and simply solved by electric means, whereas the use of pneumatics would result in complicated installations. One more advantage of electric control is the fact that the measurements for some controlled variables are directly available as electric signals, e. g., from thermocouples, Wheatstone bridges, or gas analyzers. To transduce them into pneumatic signals in any case involves the additional expense of extra components, without being able to eliminate the previous need for electrical signal amplification. Finally, concerning the actuating motors, the electric system offers the advantage of achieving any desired positioning force and valve travel by simply choosing the suitable combination of motor and gearing. Admittedly, these electric actuators are always more expensive than pneumatic ones. In addition, for the same positioning accuracy the maximum response speed of both hydraulic and pneumatic actuators will never be reached. All such electric components can be made explosion-proof; however, not without additional expenditure. The insensitivity to severe cold is another reason why the electric actuator is sometimes preferred to the pneumatic one.

3. ELECTROPNEUMATIC CONTROL

Since both electric and pneumatic control each has its advantages, the thought existed of uniting both systems to an electropneumatic control system. In this case, measuring is always done electrically and positioning pneumatically. The controller has an electric input and a pneumatic output which allows for the possibility of easily generating a pneumatic transient behavior characteristic.

Electropneumatic control should not replace purely electric or purely pneumatic control. Presently and later on, pneumatic control will be the cheapest and best solution for all secondary local control loops. For very great distances or extraordinary actuation requirements, electric control will be applied. The future of electropneumatic systems is the broad area between these two systems, particularly if compelling reasons are found which demand an electrical measurement.

These three kinds of control, therefore, have to co-exist and complement each other in a closed control system. For this purpose it is necessary, then, that all components be compatible so that they can be combined to provide the optimum technical solution for all problems.

C. The Principle of the TELEPERM-TELEPNEU System

The TELEPERM-TELEPNEU System involves an instrument product line which from its inception was based upon the problem of fulfilling all technical and operational requirements as well as possible. The principles upon which the system is based are as follows:

1. A STANDARD SYSTEM

Transmitters transform different operating variables like pressure, temperature, flow, or level into common standardized electric or pneumatic signals. Thus, it is possible to use identical controllers, recorders, and accessory components, in short; standard units for all process variables. In the United States of America, pneumatic systems were standardized on 3 to 15 pounds per square inch. In Germany, a range of 0.2 to 1.0 kg/cm^2 was selected so that, practically speaking, an international standard exists.

Conditions are not as simple with electric systems, since systems employing a—c as well as d—c have been developed in this field which are able to work with either load-independent voltages or currents. As yet, no standard for electric signals has been reached. Some years ago, NAMUR proposed that all d—c signals be standardized, but this aim has not been achieved either. The range of currents of commercially available instruments is from 1 to 200 ma. All instruments utilizing vacuum tube amplifiers naturally have small current ranges, and the strongest argument in favor of small current ranges is the fact that high line resistances, i.e. large distances, are overcome. On the other hand, the high current ranges of magnetic or transistorized instruments offer the advantage of rugged and, thus, dependable electromechanical instruments. Therefore, a good technical compromise would be to use a d—c system with a range of 0 to 50 ma, as offered by the TELEPERM-TELEPNEU System. Furthermore, it is in accordance with a recommendation by NAMUR. Standardized systems offer the advantage of more economical production and, therefore, are less expensive. When setting up a complicated control circuit, standardized systems point to a technically reasonable solution. Therefore, they are a necessary premise for the automation of modern plants in the process industries.

2. A COMPENSATING SYSTEM

It is one more feature of the TELEPERM-TELEPNEU System that all instruments are set up according to the compensating method regardless whether they are electric, pneumatic, or electropneumatic. In these instruments, input variables are compared with a controlling variable which, in turn, is proportional to the output variable of an amplifier. The amplifier control is a result of the deviation between input and comparison values. Transmission accuracy is improved as the difference between the amplifier range and the input variable range is reduced. Such compensating systems have the advantage that the output variable is independent of oscillations of power, of changes in external resistance, and of other outside influences. Therefore, the different instruments (controllers, indicators, recorders, etc.) can be tied in with the transmitters, since the compensating system provides an output value that reflects an exact function of the measured variable. Therefore, in the case of an electric system one speaks of load-independent d—c, and it would be perfectly reasonable to call the pressure signal of pneumatic instruments "load-independent". The chief advantage of the principle of these system variables is in the possibility of individually adjusting each instrument. The installation of the system is then limited to routine interconnection only, since difficult calibration is no longer required.

3. A MODULAR SYSTEM

An essential mark of a modern control product line is the use of identical modules in both the entire system as well as in the individual instruments. An outer unit-composed system comes out of separating the several functions, such as measuring, controlling, indicating, recording, and guiding, into individual instruments.

That an "inner" unit-composed system exists as well is essentially important for production as well as for maintenance in the plants. Thus, it is possible to work with standardized system variables and to construct many of the instruments on the same principle. This is especially the case where pneumatic and electropneumatic instruments are concerned, and the force balance principle is used with practically all. Thus, the same components may be used for amplification (pneumatic amplifiers with low air consumption), the subtraction for the comparison of two variables (force balances), the formation of the transient behavior (torsion restrictions), and other functions. Just like the components in the outer unit-composed system, the instruments of the inner unit-composed system are separately adjusted. This allows interchangeability during operation without necessitating a recalibration of the instruments.

4. A COMBINATION SYSTEM

The requirement for free compatibility is satisfied by the principle of standardized and modular systems. It is possible to set up the most important control operations with the TELEPERM as well as with the TELEPNEU System. These are based on three main circuits:

> Control with fixed set point,
> Ratio control,
> Cascade control.

All further circuits are simply an expansion of these three principal circuits which mainly concern improvement of process control or putting into operation.

The schematic arrangement of control with fixed set point is shown in Fig. 3 for the electric as well as for the pneumatic type of the

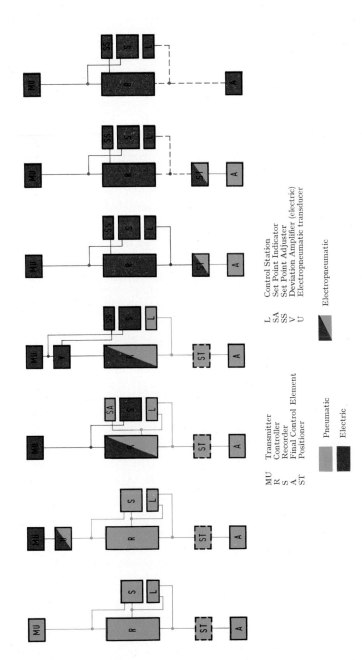

MU   Transmitter   L   Control Station
R   Controller   SA   Set Point Indicator
S   Recorder   SS   Set Point Adjuster
A   Final Control Element   V   Deviation Amplifier (electric)
ST   Positioner   U   Electropneumatic transducer

Pneumatic   Electropneumatic

Electric

Fig. 3   Basic Circuits of the Combined TELEPERM-TELEPNEU Control System.

TELEPERM-TELEPNEU System (circuits are shown at the extreme left and right). Each of these circuits consists of a transmitter, controller, instruments mounted on the panel boards such as recorder and control station and, finally, of the final control element which can be coupled with an additional position controller (positioner). The pneumatic recorder receiver always contains two measuring systems, one for the set point and one for the measured variable.

The TELEPERM and TELEPNEU Systems, however, do not represent a limited equipment product line. On the contrary, both are parts of the larger integrated system. With only some few additional units, the transfer from electric to pneumatic is made anywhere in the control circuit. The use of standardized instrumentation allows all combinations, one right next to the other in order to profit from all of the technical facilities this new way offers.

With all electropneumatic combinations, measuring is done electrically and positioning pneumatically. Thus, it is possible to unite the specific dominant characteristics of both systems. There are three basic possibilities for transducing from electric to pneumatic.

a) Transducing Following the Electric Transmitter

If measuring is to be done electrically, but the rest of control done pneumatically, an electropneumatic transducer is connected after the transmitter. This solution is particularly recommended for plants whose instrumentation is primarily pneumatic and where only a few variables have to be measured electrically. The reasons for this may be because of the great distances between the individual measuring points and the control room or in the desire to use the measured variables for controlling, for data processing, or for some other computing purposes. This combination represents the standard pneumatic solution for all measured variables expressed electrically, e.g., temperature control by thermocouples or resistance thermometers. The electric amplifier and the electropneumatic transducer in this case have to be considered as a pneumatic transmitter which is divided into two components.

As far as this technique of combined control is concerned, one would suppose it to be less attractive than a pure electric or a pure pneumatic solution, since the electropneumatic transducer causes additional time delay in the control loop. If, however, the transducer is located close to the controller, then the delay caused by this element is so small, in comparison with the other elements in the control loop, that a worse change in control dynamics is practically impossible to detect.

b) Transducing in the Controller

If the change from electric to pneumatic is performed within the controller, there are the two possibilities (Fig. 3):

In the normal case, the set point is established pneumatically and the electrical measured variable is fed to the moving coil of the controller. The control deviation is formed mechanically in the controller itself.

In the second case, the control deviation is formed in an electrical measuring circuit and, after adequate amplification, is transmitted to the moving coil of the controller.

The use of an electropneumatic controller is, in more than one way, an advantage. First, one instrument less is required compared with all other electropneumatic solutions; namely, the transducer. That this fact results in lower costs is commonly understood. However, the fact is widely ignored that control accuracy and operating safety are also improved. If the electropneumatic controller is directly mounted in the system, e.g., at the final control element, and long transmission lines exist between the plant and control room, all requirements pointing toward electric control are met. The transient behavior of the controller, however, can still be accomplished pneumatically and is the cheapest and simplest means. This solution may be of the greatest importance in the future.

c) Transducing after the Controller

The last possibility for the transducing from electric to pneumatic is between the controller itself and the final control element. Transmitter, controller, and all control room instruments are purely electrical in this solution, and only the final control element still uses compressed air as an auxiliary source of energy. The required transducer is best mounted at the diaphragm valve where it carries out the functions of the position controller, too. Its input is the signal supplied by the controller. In the TELEPERM-TELEPNEU System this is either a load-independent d—c from 0 to 50 ma or a sequence of switch impulses according to the type of controller used, Type K (continuous) or Type S (impulse). In the second case, the electro-pneumatic positioner has to take over the integration of the incoming impulses as well as the functions of transmitting and position control. The solution employing electric control and an electro-pneumatic or electrohydraulic final control element has become most modern in recent times. Often, this solution is looked upon as a standard solution for the entire processing industry. This is not so. The problems of measuring and control techniques in the process industries are so different that we must not attempt to solve them all with one standard approach. If the optimum technical and economic solutions are what are really wanted, one must have at one's disposal all of the numerous possibilities shown in Fig. 3, covering the whole range from pure electric to pure pneumatic control. This is the idea upon which the TELEPERM-TELEPNEU System is based.

D. Possibilities of Circuit Combination

The circuit combinations resulting from the modular concept of this combined electropneumatic control system are many. In the first place, there are the three basic circuits of fixed set point, cascade, and ratio control. They may all be set up in accordance with the seven combination possibilities (Fig. 3). Taking into account the transmission distances and the kind of controlled system involved, the pneumatic or electropneumatic controllers can be mounted, as desired, either in the control room or in the plant at the final control element. Finally, there are different possibilities for connecting and switching in cascade and ratio control systems, in order to achieve special solutions of operating conditions. On the whole, more than one hundred circuit combinations result from these possibilities and certainly all of today's process industry requirements can be solved by one or more of them.

1. FIXED SET POINT CONTROL

a) Pneumatic Control

The instrumentation involved in fixed set point control consists of the so-called control station, in addition to the transmitter, controller, recording or indicating receiver for the measured variable and set point, and the final control element. The indicating control station is located in the control room, directly below the indicator or recorder and it serves for directing control.

In addition, it contains one pressure element for the set point, another one for manual operation of the final control element, and a switch for transferring from automatic control to manual control. In order that this switching be bumpless (without jerky movement of the final control element), the control station has double pressure

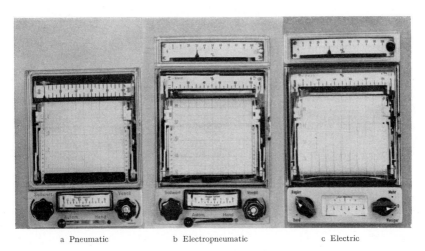

| a Pneumatic | b Electropneumatic | c Electric |

Fig. 4   Intrumentation for Control with Fixed Set Point.

gauges with which the operator can match the controller output air signal and the manual valve pressure. For switching from automatic to manual, the input feedback pressure always has to be equal to the control pressure of the final control element, otherwise for this transfer from manual to automatic an upset of the controlled variable caused by the unbalanced feedback could not possibly be avoided.

Therefore, in the TELEPNEU controllers the amplifier does not directly affect the feedback, but has an indirect effect via the indicating control station. Thus, a bumpless matching is obtained in every

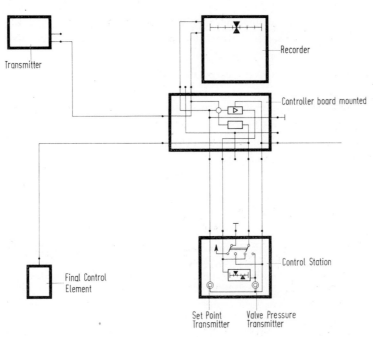

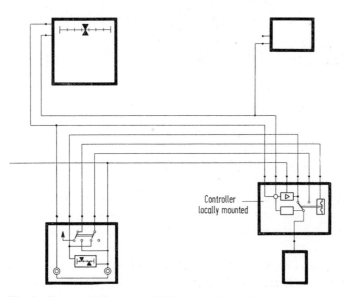

Fig. 5   Pneumatic Control with Fixed Set Point, Controller board mounted.

Fig. 6   Pneumatic Control with Fixed Set Point, Controller locally mounted.

operating condition of the control station. The two typical circuits (location of the controller in the control room and in the plant) are shown in Figs. 5 and 6.

In order that the control loop be as short as possible when the controller is located in the plant, the transfer from manual to automatic operation is carried out by a "short-circuit" relay actuated by the control station within the controller itself. The increase to five pressure lines to the control room when the controller is in the plant, compared to only two when it is located in the control room, causes a considerable increase in cost. However, this is more than paid for in better controllability.

b) Electropneumatic Control

The electropneumatic solutions of control with fixed set point are in principle like those shown for pneumatic control (Figs. 5 and 6). Of special interest are cases where there are long distances between the plant and the control room. Fig. 7 shows these combinations.

As shown in Figs. 7a and 7b, the electrical measured variable is transduced into a pneumatic actuating pressure in the control room. This is done either by the transducer or by the electropneumatic controller. The distance from the control room to the plant in this case is electrically closed on the measuring side only. These solutions will be suitable when the sensor location is far away from the other parts of the plant and the control room. These solutions are suitable for sluggish controlled systems, too, particularly if the measured variables dealt with are electric, as occurs in temperature controlled systems. In all cases where the distances are so great that the pneumatic line cannot transmit the signal, transducing from electric to pneumatic has to be done in the plant (Figs. 7c to 7e).

This can be done most simply with an electropneumatic controller at the final control element itself (Figs. 7c and 7d). Generally, it does not matter that the set point adjustment and the manual actuation of the final control element are carried out pneumatically from the control room, because any lags cannot have an effect on control dynamics (Fig. 7c).

For special cases where it may not be desirable to run pneumatic lines to the control room, electropneumatic control can be changed

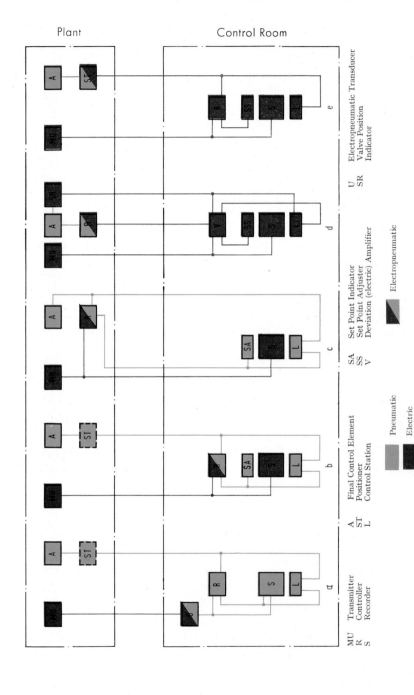

Fig. 7   Electropneumatic Control Loops for Control with Fixed Set Point.

according to Fig. 7 d; comparison of set point with measured value is done with a special measuring circuit in the control room, and the deviation is fed to the controller through an amplifier (V). Position is indicated by means of a potentiometer (SR). With switching operation to manual control, the measured variable is replaced by the position indicator signal. Manual operation is done by means of the set point adjuster. This method is extraordinarily reliable. The resulting position control maintains a commanded position by itself.

Finally, we examine circuit 7e wherein an electric controller is used and transducing is done with an electropneumatic positioner. In principle, this solution equals that in Fig. 7d. Electric controllers are naturally always located in the control room, since there are no lags from transmission lines. The advantage is based on the fact that the controller parameters can be set in the control room. This solution is, however, more expensive because an electric controller is always more expensive than a simple null balance amplifier. On the other hand, electropneumatic positioners cost about the same as electropneumatic controllers.

2. Ratio Control

One of the most important control circuits in the process industries is ratio control. It has the task of maintaining at a constant level an adjustable ratio of two operating variables. Usually, flows are the subject of this type of control. This problem is solved by a simple control; the set point is a function of the uncontrolled variable. In order to be able to adjust the ratio, a multiplying relay is installed between the transmitter for the uncontrolled variable and the controller. This device multiplies the value of the controlled variable by a constant factor set in by hand. In electric control, the multiplying device is a simple potentiometer. In pneumatics, on the other hand, the multiplying relay can only be technically accomplished by an active transmission link. The circuit with pneumatic elements is shown in Fig. 8.

The multiplying relay is schematically shown between control station and controller. The pressure of the uncontrolled variable goes to the input of the multiplying relay, the output pressure of which is the set point of the controller, and this value is indicated on the

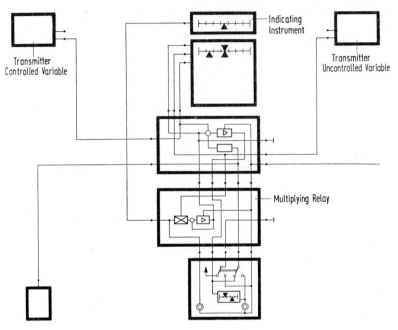

Fig. 8   Pneumatic Ratio Control.

recorder. The value set in on the left-hand pressure element of the control station is then fed as a second input to the multiplying relay. This pressure is multiplied as a constant factor by the value of the uncontrolled variable and indicated on a separate instrument above the recorder. A control of the ratio presented by this instrument is confirmed because both ratioed signals are written by the recorder. In the schematic figure the function of multiplying is represented by a rectangle with diagonals.

The circuit shown in Fig. 8 is the simplest one. When using a so-called expanded control station, the possibility exists of bumpless switching from ratio control to fixed set point control of the controlled variable (Fig. 9).

By these means the following operating conditions can be achieved: manual operation, fixed set point control, and ratio control. The bumpless transfer achieved is proved by comparing the pressures transmitted to two twin pressure gauges. Figure 10 shows the instrumentation together with the expanded control station.

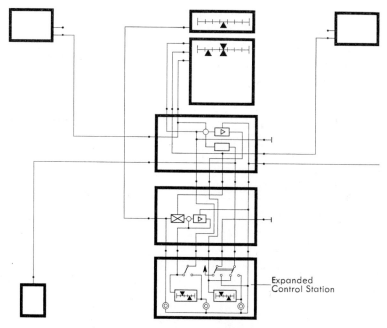

Fig. 9 Pneumatic Ratio Control with Expanded Control Station.

Naturally, ratio control can be achieved with either electropneumatic or electric instruments when, for operating reasons, measuring has to be done electrically.

There are many combination possibilities. The ones occurring most often are schematically presented in Fig. 11.

As shown in Fig. 11a, electropneumatic transducers come after the electric transmitters. The remaining instrumentation is pure pneumatic as shown in Fig. 8 or 9. Often, electropneumatic controllers will be used, which can be mounted directly at the final control element. The corresponding circuit is schematically shown in Fig. 11b. If the ratioing is to be done electrically, the resulting circuit is shown in Fig. 11c.

3. CASCADE CONTROL

One of the most efficient ways of improving the control of slow acting controlled systems with large dead time is cascade control. Its efficiency depends upon controlling the main disturbances in an auxiliary control loop without influencing the actual controlled variable. Disturbances still existing are then eliminated by the master controller actuating the set point of the secondary controller. The classic example of cascade control is the temperature control of a steam-heated furnace (Fig. 12).

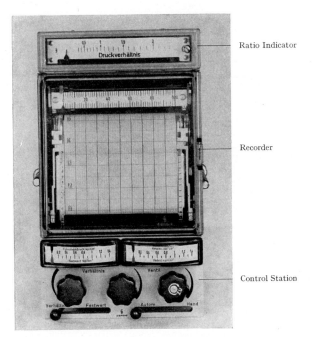

Ratio Indicator

Recorder

Control Station

Fig. 10   Instrumentation for Pneumatic Ratio Control with Expanded Control Station.

A flow controller maintains a constant flow of steam and, thereby, eliminates all disturbances stemming from variations in the steam supply. A master controller maintains the temperature control of the furnace. Either it influences the set point of the slave controller for the flow directly, or it does so through a multiplying relay. The influence of the master controller on the slave controller can be adjusted by means of the multiplying relay and, thus, the cascade is even better tuned to the controlled system than would be possible with only the parameters of the master controller. Moreover, the

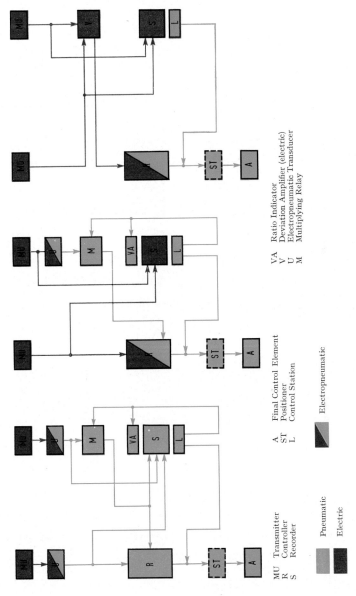

MU Transmitter
R   Controller
S   Recorder

A   Final Control Element
ST Positioner
L   Control Station

Pneumatic

Electric

Electropneumatic

VA Ratio Indicator
V   Deviation Amplifier (electric)
U   Electropneumatic Transducer
M   Multiplying Relay

Fig. 11   Schematic of Electropneumatic Ratio Controls.

influence of the master controller on the slave controller can be statically limited by the multiplying relay in order to avoid over-actuation. From the standpoint of instrument technology, the circuitry of the multiplying relay used here is the same as for the multiplying relay used in ratio control.

The simple circuit of a cascade with electropneumatic controllers without multiplying relay is shown in Fig. 13.

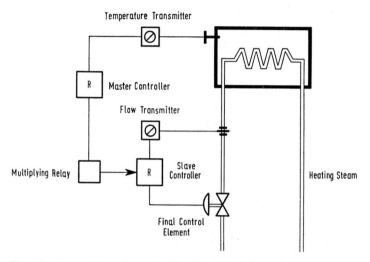

Fig. 12   Temperature Control with the Aid of Cascade Control.

The set point adjuster of the control station in the slave controller may be eliminated because this function can be taken over by the valve pressure transmitter of the slave controller. The cascade in the pure pneumatic circuit with multiplying relay is shown in Fig. 14.

The control station of the slave controller is supplemented by a coupling switch. With the aid of this device it is possible to switch without a bump from fixed set point control in the secondary loop to master control operation.

Putting such cascades into operation is not always easy, because many parameters have to be adjusted at the two controllers and,

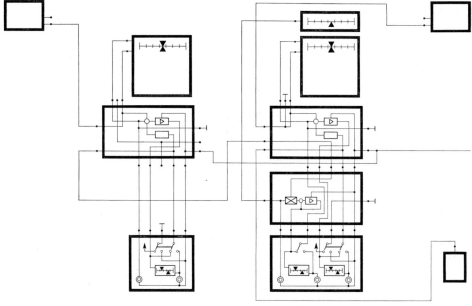

Fig. 13   Electropneumatic Cascade Control.

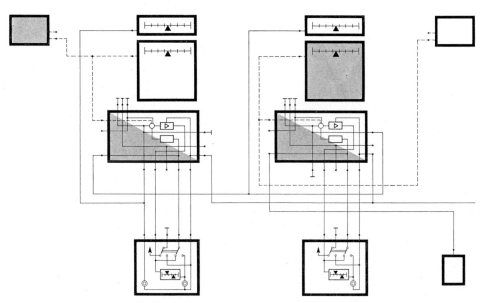

Fig. 14   Pneumatic Cascade Control with Expanded Control Station and Multiplying Relay.

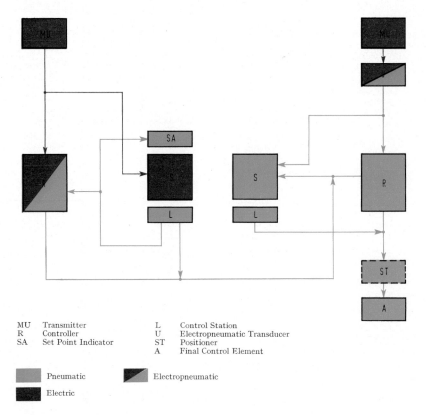

MU   Transmitter   L   Control Station
R   Controller   U   Electropneumatic Transducer
SA   Set Point Indicator   ST   Positioner
                                            A   Final Control Element

Pneumatic   Electropneumatic

Electric

Fig. 15   Schematic of Electropneumatic Cascade Control.

in some cases, at the multiplying relay, too, in order to achieve optimum control operation. In this case, it is first necessary to operate the secondary loop as a control with fixed set point and to adjust it separately until optimum operating conditions are achieved. When minimum multiplying relay influence exists, it is then switched bump-free to master control operation through the coupling switch. Now, the master control loop can, in its turn, be adjusted to its optimum by setting the parameters at the controller and the degree of influence at the multiplying relay accordingly.

Figure 15 shows schematically still another typical electropneumatic combination possibility. Since the secondary loop generally means quick control, its instrumentation with pneumatic components is

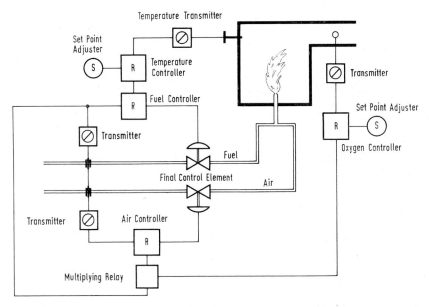

Fig. 16   Fuel Control of a Furnace Illustrating Cascade Ratio Control.

especially feasible. The circuit shown in Fig. 15 will, therefore, be the combination used most often. In most cases the transmitter and the electropneumatic transducer in the secondary loop will be replaced by a pneumatic instrument.

4. CASCADE RATIO CONTROL

The guiding of a control loop by a master controller may be applied to ratio control as well. A case often occurring for this type of control is in combustion control (Fig. 16).

Usually, two cascade systems are used. The first one is the temperature cascade, where the set point of the fuel flow controller is changed by the temperature controller. The second one is a ratio cascade. Here, a master controller corrects the fuel-air ratio according to the percentage of oxygen of the flue gas.

Here, too, there are a large number of combination possibilities. Even with purely pneumatic solutions several ways of doing things are possible. They differ particularly with respect to operation, acceptability, and putting into operation. Because the putting into

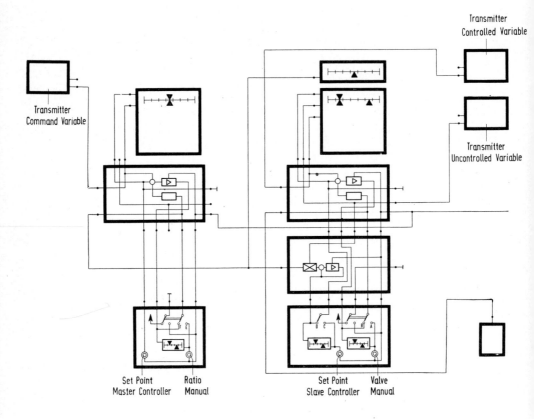

Transmitter
Controlled Variable

Transmitter
Command Variable

Transmitter
Uncontrolled Variable

Set Point   Ratio
Master Controller   Manual

Set Point   Valve
Slave Controller   Manual

Switch Positions: A   Manual Operation of Valve
                   BC   Control with Fixed Set Point of Slave Circuit
                   BDE   Ratio Control with Manual Ratio Setting
                   BDF   Ratio Control with Commanded Ratio

Fig. 17   Pneumatic Cascade Ratio Control with Expanded Control Station.

operation and adjusting of the control parameters are rather complicated, the expanded arrangement with a coupling switch should
prevail as a standard solution (Fig. 17).

Here, four different operating conditions have to be differentiated;
namely, manual operation of the valve, fixed set point control of the
secondary loop, ratio control with adjustable ratio, and ratio control
with guided ratio. The transfer to the different operating conditions

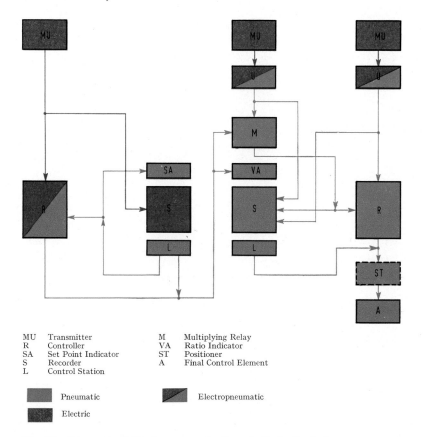

MU	Transmitter	M	Multiplying Relay
R	Controller	VA	Ratio Indicator
SA	Set Point Indicator	ST	Positioner
S	Recorder	A	Final Control Element
L	Control Station		

Pneumatic   Electropneumatic

Electric

Fig. 18   Schematic of Electropneumatic Cascade Ratio Control.

is always carried out completely bump-free with the control stations described, with an exact assimilation possible through use of the double pressure gauges.

The scheme of an electropneumatic version of cascade ratio control is shown in Fig. 18. It may serve as an example for many solutions, since the number of solution combinations is extremely high with the many instruments used.

II. STRUCTURAL ELEMENTS

A. Pneumatic Force Balance

1. Scope

The pneumatic force balance is the reference element of controllers, positioners, and valve position indicators. Air pressures are converted to torque effects by means of bellows and compared to each other or to a mechanical momentum transmitted by a torsion spring. Deviations from equilibrium cause a deflection on the force balance, the amount and direction of which are felt by a pneumatic pickup (nozzle).

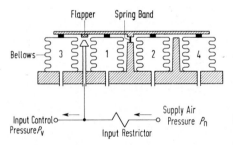

Fig. 19   Scheme of a Pneumatic Force Balance.

2. Principle and Mode of Operation

The performance may be explained with the aid of a force balance having four bellows (Fig. 19): four bellows are rigidly mounted on one of their ends and are linked at their free ends to a scale beam. The levers and the effective areas of the bellows are so dimensioned that equal pressures in the pair of bellows made up of 1 and 2 and in the pair made up of 3 and 4 result in zero momentum about the fulcrum. Differences in pressure in one or both pairs of bellows, however, cause a resultant momentum (M_{RES}) around the fulcrum.

This momentum causes a deflection of the scale beam from the zero position.

The scale beam is linked to a flapper which controls the air flow through a nozzle. The supply air is at constant pressure p_n through a fixed input restrictor. Pressure p_v exists between the input restrictor and the nozzle and will be a result of the nozzle throttling, i.e., corresponding to the resultant torque at the scale beam. This relationship is shown in Fig. 20.

For reasons of accuracy and dynamic sensitivity it is best to eliminate all but a small part in the mid-range of this curve for

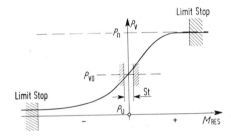

Fig. 20   Characteristic Curve of Input Control.

use in adjusting the amplifier which follows. Therefore, for the amplifier of the TELEPNEU System, a medium operating point of 0.6 kg/cm² was chosen and an actuating range of approximately 0.04 kg/cm². In order to prevent damage to the bellows caused by overranging, the deflection of the scale beam is limited on either side. On the one side, the nozzle itself serves as a stop and on the other side, a special stop is attached (Fig. 19).

3. MODELS

Force balances are used in five different models (Fig. 21):

a) The Five-Bellows Force Balance

The five-bellows force balance is used both in proportional-plus-reset-action and in proportional-plus-reset-plus-rate action plug-in controllers. By comparing the pressures of the two inner bellows

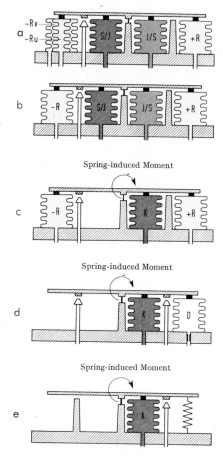

Spring-induced Moment

Spring-induced Moment

Spring-induced Moment

D   Damping Bellows
K   Control Pressure Bellows
J   Measured Variable Pressure
S   Set Point Pressure
R   Feedback
R_v Feedback, delayed
R_u Feedback, undelayed

Fig. 21   Types of Force Balances.

a   Five-Bellows Force Balance
b   Four-Bellows Force Balance
c   Three-Bellows Force Balance
d   Two-Bellows Force Balance
e   Single-Bellows Force Balance

(set point and measured variable bellows), deviation in control is measured. The two outer bellows (feedback bellows) provide the desired transient behavior. The negative feedback element (—R) is built as a double bellows. Its outer bellows receives the same pressure as its inner one which is, however, time delayed in order to achieve a rate action. By these means the stability of the controller is protected against self-induced oscillations.

b) The Four-Bellows Force Balance

The four-bellows force balance is used in the reset action controller (flow controller). Since a rate action is not desired in this case, the negative feedback element is a single bellows.

c) The Three-Bellows Force Balance

This device is the reference element in a single-acting positioner. The torque effect of the control pressure bellows is balanced against the moment created by the valve position through a torque spring at the force balance. The two outer bellows again serve as feedback.

d) The Two-Bellows Force Balance

This type is required for double-acting positioner as required in springless diaphragm motors or piston mechanisms. In place of the stop, a second nozzle is used to provide the required counter working pressure. A feedback is not provided in this case. The outer bellows serves as damping. Thus, disturbing oscillations are prevented that might result at the force balance by reactions of the nozzles.

e) The Single-Bellows Force Balance

This type of force balance is provided for the valve position transmitter. Unlike the positioners, the moment transmitted by the torque

1 Base
2 Limit Stop
3 Nozzle with Flapper
4 Bellows
5 Eccentric
6 Scale Beam

Fig. 22   Pneumatic Force Balance.

spring is the input variable which is balanced against the torque created by the control pressure bellows. To insure the stability of the force balance, an additional spring is mounted in parallel to the bellows.

4. DESIGN AND ASSEMBLY

The design of the force balances can be seen in Figs. 22 to 24. Instead of a force balance with three or less bellows, one with four bellows can be used when needed. Nozzles or stops are added according to requirements (Fig. 21).

The scale beam is supported without friction in two spring bands and the bellows are connected to the beam by means of eccentrics.

Thus, it is possible to finely adjust the levers by turning the eccentrics. This step is necessary to adjust the torques.

The force balances are plugged into the corresponding devices as complete modules and fastened with four screws. The air connections are sealed with "O" rings.

The force balances are rugged elements, not affected by disturbances. Therefore, it is not necessary to take them apart. Their simple design allows for easy replacement of defective parts as required. When disassembling and re-assembling the force balance, the following instructions should be observed:

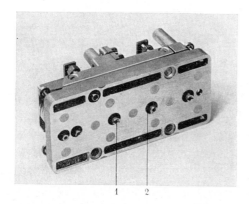

1 Supply Air Connection

2 "O" Rings

Fig. 23   Connection Side of the Five-Bellows Force Balance.

Fig. 24   Components of a Five-Bellows Force Balance.

After loosening the hold-down screws for the spring bands and bellows, the scale beam may be removed. The bellows are screwed to the base plate. Loosening and tightening is done from below with a screwdriver.

When re-assembling, care must be taken that the scale beam is parallel to the base plate in order to avoid canting of the nozzle and flapper. The hold-down screws for the eccentrics must be tightened until noticeable resistance is felt from the spring washers located below. The spring washer should not be completely compressed.

5. ADJUSTING AND TESTING

The force balances are the actual measuring elements of the controllers, positioners, and position transmitters. Therefore, they have to be very carefully tested and adjusted. They are delivered as adjusted units and may be exchanged without recalibration. However, should it be necessary to replace defective bellows, then the required adjustments are to be carried out as follows:

The tightness of the bellows and the complete mating of the nozzle and flapper have to be checked. The zero point has to be adjusted by turning the nozzle and the same has to be done with the effective torques of the bellows by shifting their links on the scale beam.

For expediency, a compensating circuit should be used for calibration (Figs. 25 to 29). This circuit insures stable measured variables, accelerates calibration and makes it easier. To set up this test circuit, the force balances are connected to test pedestals by means of hose sockets. Class 1 pressure gauges currently on the market may be used. A U-tube water-filled manometer is recommended as a differential pressure gauge. The standard supply air pressure is $1.4 \ kg/cm^2$. For checking and adjustment, the following sequence is recommended:

a) The Five-Bellows Force Balance

Adjusting is done according to the test circuit shown in Fig. 25. Preadjusting the nozzle: With the bellows deflated, the distance between nozzle and flapper is adjusted by turning the nozzle until a definite input control pressure p_v is obtained.

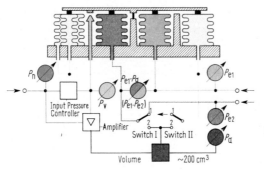

Fig. 25   Test Circuit for a
Five-Bellows Force
Balance.

Switches I and II in position 1:

Adjust p_{e1} and p_{e2} to 0 kg/cm².

Turn nozzle until p_v equals 0.6 kg/cm².

Testing the nozzle for complete closing: When pressing the flapper
against the nozzle, p_v should be greater than 1 kg/cm².
Adjusting the stop: The stop is turned until its distance from the
stop plate is about 0.5 mm.
Measuring the actuating range: With deflated feedback bellows, the
pressure differential in the inner bellows must be ascertained which
is necessary to produce amplifier output pressure changes from
0.2 to 1.0 kg/cm². This pressure differential is the actuating range
of the force balance. Usually, this range is referred to the standard
pressure range of 0.8 kg/cm² and then given as a percentage.

Adjust p_{e2} to 0.6 kg/cm².

Increase p_{e1} until p_a equals 0.2 kg/cm².

Increase p_{e1} further until p_a equals 1.0 kg/cm².

Measure the differential pressure of the inner bellows necessary to
pass this pressure range (0.8 kg/cm²) of p_a.
Adjusting the inner bellows: When calibrating the inner bellows,
the lever arms are so adjusted that equal pressures cause equal
torques. With deflated feedback bellows, an adjustable input pressure is applied to the inner bellows opposed to the nozzle. The output
pressure of the amplifier is switched to the other inner bellows so
that a countercoupled system results.

Now balancing has to be done so that with a change in the inlet pressure of 0.2 to 1.0 kg/cm², the outlet pressure of the amplifier covers a range reduced by the actuating range.

> Switch I in position 2, switch II in position 1:
> Adjust p_{e1} to 0.2 kg/cm².

Adjust nozzle so that difference in pressure between the inner bellows disappears.

> Set p_{e1} to 1.0 kg/cm².

Adjust the lever arms of the inner bellows by turning the eccentrics until the difference in pressure between the two inner bellows equals the actuating range. The following has to be observed when making this adjustment as well as for adjusting the outer bellows, too:

After *every* move of an eccentric, the nozzle has to be readjusted so that the difference in pressure of the inner bellows at p_{e1} equal to 0.2 kg/cm² disappears.

Adjusting the outer bellows: the outer bellows are so adjusted that the force balance is in unstable equilibrium with maximum feedback for all amplifier output pressures. The balancing is so accomplished that, with a bias in the + R feedback bellows, a large enough regeneration feedback results to just compensate the actuating range.

> Switches I and II in position 2:
> Adjust p_{e1} to 0.2 kg/cm².

Adjust nozzle so that the pressure differential between the inner bellows disappears.

> Adjust p_{e1} to 1.0 kg/cm².

Adjust outer bellows by so turning eccentrics that the pressure differential of the inner bellows equals zero.

When the calibration is finished, coat all eccentrics and set screws with lacquer.

b) The Four-Bellows Force Balance

The calibration of the four-bellows force balance is accomplished according to the test circuit shown in Fig. 26 and in the same manner as the five-bellows force balance.

c) The Three-Bellows Force Balance

The inner bellows of the force balance is not to be adjusted. The balancing of its torque with that of the torque spring is done after mounting the positioner at the diaphragm valve. Testing and adjusting are carried out as shown in the diagram of Fig. 27.

Preadjustment of the nozzle: The nozzle is adjusted so that with a medium pressure in the outer bellows, a corresponding medium amplifier outlet pressure results.

Set p_e to 0.6 kg/cm².

Adjust nozzle so that pressure differential in the two outer bellows disappears.

Check the nozzle for tightness and set the stop as was done for the five-bellows force balance.

Adjusting the outer bellows: The outer bellows are so balanced that, with equal pressures, the force balance is in unstable equilibrium. The actuating range is thus compensated by the feedback.

Set p_e to 0.2 kg/cm².

Turn the nozzle until pressure differential in both outer bellows disappears.

Set p_e to 1.0 kg/cm².

Adjust outer bellows by turning the eccentrics so that the pressure differential similarly disappears.

d) The Two-Bellows Force Balance

Only the two nozzles are adjusted. The balancing of the inner bellows torque with the helical spring torque is done when mounting the positioners at the diaphragm valve. The outer bellows need not be adjusted. The test circuit is as shown in Fig. 28.

Adjusting the nozzles: Both nozzles are adjusted by turning them until pressures p_{v1} and p_{v2} downstream from the input restrictors are equal to 0.7 kg/cm².

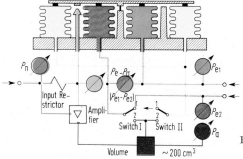

Fig. 26 Test Circuit for a Four-Bellows Force Balance.

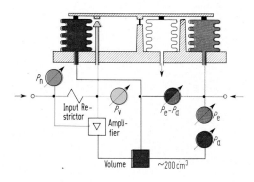

Fig. 27 Test Circuit for a Three-Bellows Force Balance.

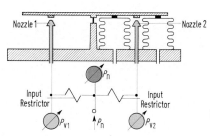

Fig. 28 Test Circuit for a Two-Bellows Force Balance.

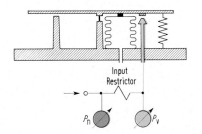

Fig. 29 Test Circuit for a Single-Bellows Force Balance.

Checking of nozzles for tightness: Testing is done as for the five-bellows force balance.

e) The One-Bellows Force Balance

Only the nozzle is adjusted to medium input pressure of 0.6 kg/cm^2 as shown for the circuit in Fig. 29.
Checking the nozzle for tightness and adjusting the stop are done in the usual manner.

6. MAINTENANCE

Maintenance of the force balances during operation is not necessary. The flapper should be checked from time to time for dirt.

7. TECHNICAL DATA

Effective area of the individual bellows . . . .   2.5 cm^2

Effective area of the inner bellows with double
   bellows . . . .   0.5 cm^2

Ratio of the lever arms between the inner pair
   of bellows and the outer pair of bellows . . .   1 : 3

Diameter of the nozzle . . . .   1.8 mm

Flapper travel . . . . about   0.005 mm

Actuating ranges of the force balances. . . . . $<0.3\%$

B. Pneumatic Amplifier

1. SCOPE

The pneumatic amplifier is used in controllers, multiplying relays, positioners, valve position indicators, and transmitters. It acts as a pressure and power amplifier. The pressure amplification increases the sensitivity of the instruments and insures a high accuracy of measuring and controllability. Power amplification is needed for rapid actuation of the associated instruments, especially of the final control elements.

2. Principle and Mode of Operation

The amplifier works on the principle of negligibly low air consumption. The input variable is the control pressure of the flapper-nozzle pick-up. Fig. 30 shows the mode of operation.

A change in input pressure creates an up or down movement of the intermediate plate through the effective area of the upper bellows and the elasticity of the spring system, corresponding to the increase or decrease of the input pressure. Thus, the double ball valve

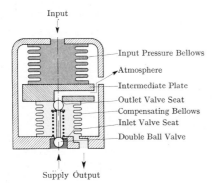

Input

Input Pressure Bellows
Atmosphere
Intermediate Plate
Outlet Valve Seat
Compensating Bellows
Inlet Valve Seat
Double Ball Valve

Supply Output

Fig. 30   Schematic Diagram of Pneumatic Amplifier according to the Low Air Consumption Principle.

is so actuated that it connects the amplifier output to either the supply or to the atmosphere. The intermediate plate is only in equilibrium when the ratio of output to input pressure corresponds to the effective areas of the upper and the lower bellows. By this arrangement, the amplifier is a controller which regulates the output pressure to a value determined only by the input pressure and the amplification factor. This type of control prevents large output pressure changes caused by changes in supply pressure or temperature.

The amplifier has a 20-fold amplification of pressure. To achieve an amplifier output pressure in the range of 0.2 kg/cm² to 1.0 kg/cm², a change in input pressure of 0.04 kg/cm² is required. This difference in pressure of 0.04 kg/cm² is the static actuating range.

For reasons of accuracy and dynamic sensitivity, the mid-scale operating point of the input pressure to the amplifier is set to 0.6 kg/cm². This so-called zero point is set by adjusting a zero point spring with a set screw (Fig. 31).

A special property of the amplifier is the change in the effective output air flow within an input pressure range of about 0.4 kg/cm². This dynamic actuating range is thus ten times as large as the static actuating range. The term "dynamic actuating range" indicates that the maximum output air flow of the amplifier is reached only after a change in the input pressure of about 0.4 kg/cm². The flow then amounts to about 50 Std. l/min. As a result of this amplifier quality, the positioning speed of the diaphragm motor reaches its

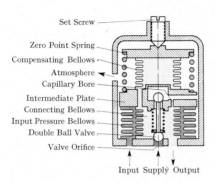

Fig. 31   Design of the Pneumatic Amplifier.

highest value only with control deviations of about 0.04 kg/cm² in the TELEPNEU controllers. The damping of controllers and control loops is improved by these means (progressive control).

3. DESIGN AND ASSEMBLY

Fig. 31 shows a schematic cross-section of the amplifier. All external connections are tapped holes in the socket base. In addition, a connecting bellows is integral with the pressure chamber of the compensating bellows. Compensating and connecting bellows both have the same cross-section and are connected by four passages. The connecting bellows also exerts a force on the intermediate plate as a result of the amplifier output pressure. This force counteracts that of the compensating bellows but is smaller, depending upon the cross-section of the bottom valve seat. Thus, a 20-fold pressure amplification is made possible with a small difference between the effective areas of input pressure and compensating bellows.

The pressure chamber of the connecting bellows is connected to the atmosphere via a capillary-size hole. Thus, a small amount of air leaks to the atmosphere at the amplifier output. The lower valve seat is therefore always a little open, which makes the output pressure have a steady dependence on the input pressure throughout the entire amplifier actuating range.

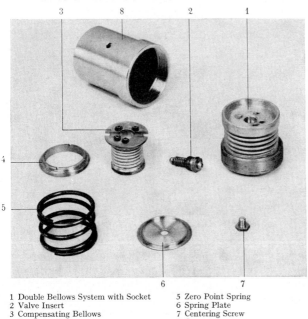

1 Double Bellows System with Socket	5 Zero Point Spring
2 Valve Insert	6 Spring Plate
3 Compensating Bellows	7 Centering Screw
4 Retaining Ring	8 Cover

Fig. 32   Components of the Pneumatic Amplifier.

The zero point spring for adjusting the mid-scale operating point is placed in parallel with the compensating bellows and it is tensioned by turning a set screw.

The amplifier assembly is seen in Fig. 32. The valve seat is screwed into the socket containing the lower double bellows. The compensating bellows is mounted on top of this and is pulled down with a retaining ring. "O" rings are installed beforehand and seal the overflow passages from the atmosphere. After installing the zero point spring, the spring plate is tightened against the compensating

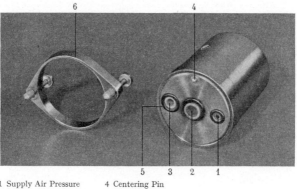

1 Supply Air Pressure   4 Centering Pin
2 Inlet Pressure   5 "O" Ring
3 Outlet Pressure   6 Flange with Hold-Down Screws

Fig. 33   Assembled Pneumatic Amplifier.

bellows with the centering screw. All inner parts now form a solidly interconnected unit. A cover screws onto the outer threaded portion of the socket, forms the strength member with the socket, and protects the inner parts against damage. A bored hole connects the outlet valve to the atmosphere. A flange with two hold-down screws fastens the completely assembled plug-in unit to the base plates of the different instruments (Fig. 33). The three connecting holes for input, supply and output pressures are sealed with "O" rings against the surrounding air pressure. The guide pin matches corresponding holes in the instrument base plates and, thus, insures correct installation.

4. Adjusting and Testing

The mid-scale operating point of the amplifier will be adjusted. Pressure amplification and constant air consumption are to be tested.

The adjusting and test circuit is shown in Fig. 34.

a) Adjusting the Operating Point and Testing the Air Consumption

The supply pressure is set to 1.4 kg/cm^2 and the inlet pressure to 0.6 kg/cm^2. The set screw is turned until the outlet pressure is also 0.6 kg/cm^2. The outlet air flow indicated on the flowmeter may be a maximum of 1.5 Std. l/min.

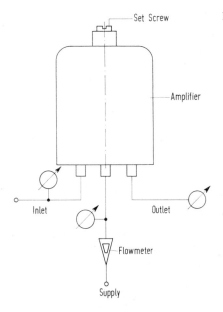

Fig. 34 Adjusting and Testing Circuit
for the Pneumatic Amplifier.

b) Testing the Amplification

Set inlet pressure to 0.58 kg/cm². The outlet pressure must be equal to or smaller than 0.2 kg/cm².

Increase inlet pressure to 0.62 kg/cm². The outlet pressure must be equal to or greater than 1.0 kg/cm².

5. MAINTENANCE

The pneumatic amplifier needs no special maintenance.

6. TECHNICAL DATA

Normal supply pressure . . . . 1.4 kg/cm²
Maximum supply pressure . . . . 2.0 kg/cm²
Air consumption . . . . 1.5 Std. l/min
Maximum outlet air flow . . . . $\geq$ 50 Std. l/min
Inlet pressure mid-scale operating point . . 0.6 kg/cm²
Static pressure amplification 20

C. Precision Pressure Transmitter

The precision pressure transmitter is used in all places where a pressure is set "manually" and must be kept exactly at a constant level. Therefore, it is predominantly used in indicating control stations.

1. PRINCIPLE OF OPERATION

The precision pressure transmitter (Fig. 35) works on the principle of low air consumption.

The mode of operation is illustrated by Fig. 36. The measuring spring is compressed by the knob that serves for adjusting a desired outlet pressure. The compressed spring exerts a force on the intermediate plate. Through the effect of the outlet pressure on the compensating bellows, a force results on the intermediate plate that counteracts the force of the compressed spring. A difference occurring between the force of the spring and that of the pressure

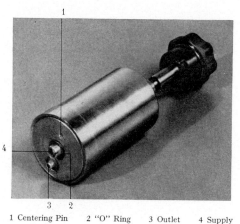

Fig. 35   Precision Pressure Transmitter according to the Low Air Consumption Principle.

1 Centering Pin   2 "O" Ring   3 Outlet   4 Supply

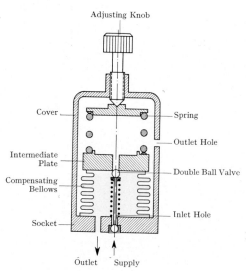

Fig. 36   Schematic Diagram of the Precision Pressure Transmitter.

changes the position of the double ball valve until equilibrium in these forces is again established. During this action, the pressure chamber of the compensating bellows is temporarily connected with the supply or the atmosphere until the desired output pressure is obtained. The precision pressure transmitter works as a proportional action controller, whose set point is the force of the spring, and whose actual value is the pressure. Changes in controlled outlet

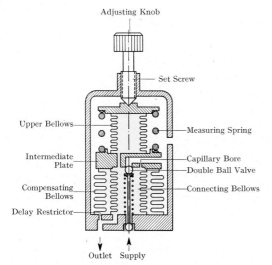

Fig. 37   Design of the Precision Pressure Transmitter.

pressure caused by changes in the supply pressure or by temperature are thus largely suppressed.

2. TECHNICAL PERFORMANCE

The construction of the precision pressure transmitter is shown in Fig. 37. For reasons of stability, a change in outlet pressure should only have a delayed effect on the compensating bellows. Therefore, a connecting bellows is built into the compensating bellows. Any remaining undelayed compensating force at the intermediate plate, coming from the inner bellows, is counteracted by an upper bellows of an equal size.

A capillary bore connects the pressure chamber of the connecting bellows with the atmosphere. Therefore, a small amount of air always leaks out to the atmosphere. This causes the lower valve seat to always be a little opened, resulting in a steady dependence of the output pressure on the tension in the measuring spring.

The precision pressure transmitter consists of several structural units (Fig. 38). The bottom double bellows is soft soldered pressure tight to the socket and the intermediate plate. The upper bellows is mounted on this plate and fastened with the retaining ring. The two

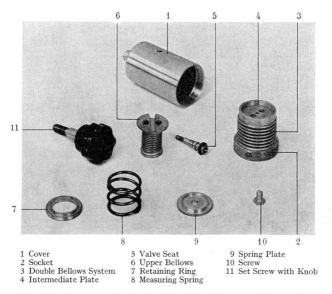

1 Cover	5 Valve Seat	9 Spring Plate
2 Socket	6 Upper Bellows	10 Screw
3 Double Bellows System	7 Retaining Ring	11 Set Screw with Knob
4 Intermediate Plate	8 Measuring Spring	

Fig. 38   Components of the Precision Pressure Transmitter.

overflow holes are made tight by "O" rings that are placed in between. The measuring spring and its plate are guided by the centering pin. The transmission of force is closed by the set screw and by the cover which is screwed to the socket. The valve seat and the delay restrictor are screwed into the socket. The precision pressure transmitter, like other elements, is built as a plug-in unit. A guide pin insures correct installation. Contact force against the base plates of the control stations results from a pressure screw. On one side, this screw is supported by the cover of the transmitter, and on the other side, by the front plate of the control station and, thus, causes a tight seal against the "O" rings.

In order to avoid an undesired shift in the transmitter parts, safety knobs may also be used instead of the usual ones. These knobs must first be pulled before the transmitter can be adjusted.

3. TESTING

Adjustment of the precision pressure transmitter is not necessary. The testing is limited to checking the supply pressure and load relationships, as well as checking the air consumption. In Fig. 39, a test circuit is shown. The transmitter is mounted on a base made for testing. A very accurate measuring instrument must be used for the outlet pressure because of the great accuracy of the pressure transmitter.

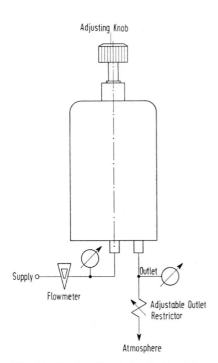

Fig. 39 Testing Circuit for the Precision Pressure Transmitter.

a) Testing Air Consumption

With a supply pressure of 1.4 kg/cm² and an outlet pressure of 1.0 kg/cm², the air consumption may be 1.5 Std. l/min and with an outlet pressure of 0.1 kg/cm², it may be a maximum of 0.4 Std. l/min.

b) Testing the Dependence on the Supply Pressure

If the supply pressure of 1.4 kg/cm² is changed by $\pm$ 0.2 kg/cm², the change in a mid-scale outlet pressure of 0.6 kg/cm² may not be greater than ± 0.003 kg/cm².

c) Testing the Dependence on Load

Supply pressure 1.4 kg/cm².

The adjustable outlet restrictor is opened until a flow of 6 Std. l/min is obtained. Then a mid-scale outlet pressure of 0.6 kg/cm² may decrease by a maximum of 0.07 kg/cm².

In operation, precision pressure transmitter needs no maintenance.

4. TECHNICAL DATA

Normal supply pressure . . . . 1.4 kg/cm²

Maximum supply pressure . . . . 2.0 kg/cm²

Maximum air consumption . . . . <1.5 Std. 1/min

Adjustment range . . . . 0 to 1.3 kg/cm²

Number of screw turns for the range of
0.2 to 1.0 kg/cm² 4

Function of input pressure with a supply pressure of 1.4 kg/cm²:

$$\frac{0.0015 \text{ kg/cm}^2 \text{ change in outlet pressure}}{0.1 \text{ kg/cm}^2 \text{ change in supply pressure}}$$

Function of load with a supply pressure of 1.4 kg/cm² between running without a load and 6 Std. 1/min:

$$\frac{0.01 \text{ kg/cm}^2 \text{ change in outlet pressure}}{1 \text{ Std. 1/min change in outlet air flow}}$$

Function of temperature with a supply pressure of 1.4 kg/cm² in the temperature range of 25 to 55°C:

$$\frac{0.0035 \text{ kg/cm}^2 \text{ change in outlet pressure}}{10°C \text{ change in temperature}}$$

D. Restrictors

1. THE ADJUSTMENT OF CONTROL PARAMETERS BY ADJUSTABLE RESTRICTIONS

Proportional band, reset and rate action of controllers are adjusted with restrictors having continuously adjustable resistances.

For changing the proportional band, the proportional action restrictor is placed between the amplifier outlet and the controller feedback.

It consists of a fixed and an adjustable restrictor by means of which the ratio between the amplifier outlet pressure and the feedback pressure may be changed (pressure divider).

The reset and rate action restrictors together form adjustable time units with the following capacities; they are switched into the feedback branch of the controller and, thus, determine the transient behavior.

2. Mode of Operation

a) The Division of Pressure with the Proportional-plus-reset and Proportional-plus-reset-plus-rate Action Controller

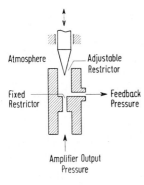

Fig. 40

Pressure Divider for the PI and PID Controller.

With the proportional-plus-reset action controller and the proportional-plus-reset-plus-rate action controller, the adjustment of the proportional band is done by a division of pressure, where the constantly flowing air discharges to the atmosphere (Fig. 40).

The amplifier outlet pressure is in front of the fixed restrictor, and the feedback pressure is between the fixed and adjustable restrictors. In order not to endanger the stability of the controller, no perceptible delays may occur between amplifier outlet pressure and the feedback pressure. The fixed restrictor must have a relatively wide diameter in order to obtain a sufficient flow of air. This is also true for the adjustable restrictor which is, therefore, a needle valve. The hole which bleeds off the feedback pressure lies directly over the fixed restrictor. This has the effect that with a wide open needle valve and a strong air flow through the fixed restrictor, a suction results at the feedback pressure opening. The fixed restrictor then acts as an injector nozzle.

The steady rate characteristic of the pressure division is thus linearized (Fig. 41, curve a). Besides that, the feedback pressure reaches atmospheric pressure with a small opening of the needle valve. Without the injector effect, the proportional band restrictor would have a characteristic corresponding to curve b, Fig. 41.

b) The Division of Pressure with the Proportional Band Controller

With the proportional band controller, too, proportional band range is accomplished by a pressure dividing arrangement, where the air

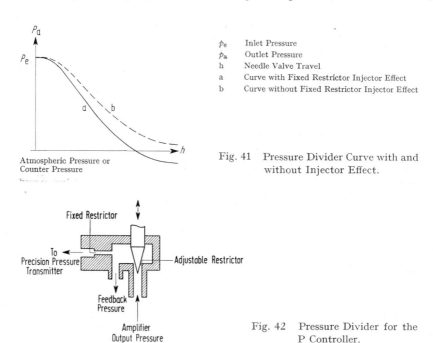

p_e	Inlet Pressure
p_a	Outlet Pressure
h	Needle Valve Travel
a	Curve with Fixed Restrictor Injector Effect
b	Curve without Fixed Restrictor Injector Effect

Fig. 41   Pressure Divider Curve with and without Injector Effect.

Fig. 42   Pressure Divider for the P Controller.

does not bleed out to the atmosphere, but to an adjustable pressure level (Fig. 42).

This is necessary because, with the proportional band controller, the intersection of the pressure division characteristics should not be fixed at an atmospheric level, but, rather, at an arbitrary adjustable value within the entire pressure range.

In this case, the amplifier outlet pressure here is in front of the adjustable restrictor. A precision pressure transmitter built into the restrictor block is connected in back of the fixed restrictor and produces the adjustable counter pressure level.

Should the amplifier output pressure be greater than the feedback pressure, the air bleeds out against this pressure level. Should the feedback pressure, on the other hand, be greater than the amplifier output pressure, the direction of flow is reversed. Again, the adjustable restrictor is a needle valve.

c) The Time Delay Restrictors

The rate and reset times of the controllers result from the delay of their feedback pressures. To achieve large adjusting ranges, the derivative action restrictor for adjusting the rate time and the

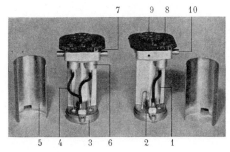

1 Restrictor Tube
2 Capillary Tube
3 Socket
4 Plastic Hose
5 Protecting Case
6 Coupling
7 Indicator
8 Dial Plate
9 Dial Face
10 Adjusting Screw

Fig. 43   PI and PID Restrictor Blocks, Protecting Cover Removed.

integral action restrictor for adjusting the reset time are built as torsion restrictions. These are thin-walled, seamless tubes made of an elastic material (copper beryllium) which are permanently deformed after being compressed to a small diameter.

Twisting these tubes around their longitudinal axes (Fig. 43) produces an elastic change in the cross-section area and, thus, causes a change in resistance to the air flow. In order to increase the delay times, storage volumes are inserted between the torsion restrictors and the feedback bellows. These, however, are located outside of the restrictor blocks in the base plates of the controllers.

3. Types of Restrictor Devices

The adjustable restrictors are assembled as complete restrictor devices called "restrictor blocks." The four types of controllers in the Telepneu line differ in their static and dynamic transfer behavior. Since this transfer behavior results exclusively from adjustable restrictors, it is possible to set up all controllers on a modular basis utilizing standard components and achieve the specific properties solely through the corresponding restrictor type. The four different restrictor types are defined according to the properties of each controller and are, therefore, so named:

Proportional, reset, proportional-plus-reset and proportional-plus-reset-plus-rate action restrictors (Fig. 44).

The reset action restrictor block is the delay restriction of the

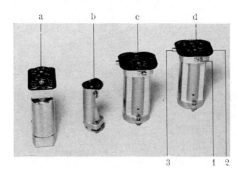

a P Restrictor Block
b I Restrictor Block
c PI Restrictor Block
d PID Restrictor Block

1 P Adjustment
2 D Adjustment
3 I Adjustment

Fig. 44   The Restrictor Units.

flow controller which has essentially the characteristic transient behavior of a reset action controller.

In turn, restrictor blocks contain the same components; namely, needle valves and torsion restrictors.

The proportional-plus-reset and the proportional-plus-reset-plus-rate action restrictor blocks have a needle valve each and one or two torsion restrictors. The reset action restrictor block, however, has only one torsion restrictor. Accordingly, the proportional action restrictor block contains only the needle valve. For providing an adjustable counter-acting pressure level, an additional precision pressure transmitter is included.

Assembling all control parameter adjustments in the restrictor blocks offers great operating and technical advantages; for example, a proportional-plus-reset action controller can be expanded to a proportional-plus-reset-plus-rate action controller by simply exchanging the restrictor block, without necessitating recalibrations or zero point corrections.

4. DESIGN

The restrictor blocks are mounted on the controller base plates and fastened by two screws which cannot be lost (Fig. 43).

On the underside are the connections, sealed by "O" rings, to the corresponding holes on the controller base plates (Fig. 45). The restrictors are adjusted with a screwdriver at the adjusting screws for proportional band (P), the rate time (D), and the reset time (I), as shown in Fig. 44.

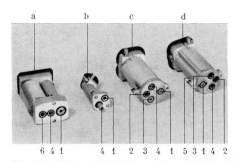

a P Restrictor Block
b I Restrictor Block
c PI Restrictor Block
d PID Restrictor Block

1 Amplifier Outlet
2 Negative Feedback (Inner Bellows)
3 Negative Feedback (Outer Bellows)
4 Positive Feedback
5 Atmosphere
6 Air Supply

Fig. 45   External Air Connections to the Restrictor Blocks.

Basically, increasing values are obtained by turning the screws clockwise.

a) Needle Valves

The needle valves are placed in the columns of the restrictor blocks. The needle is spring-mounted in a sleeve. To avoid hysteresis, the sleeve is always under the tension of a second spring which continually loads the movement screw of the sleeve on one side. The sleeve is moved by a worm gear and a gear coupling by turning the proportional band adjusting screw. The dial of the proportional restrictor is bolted to the worm gear after adjustment.

The fixed restrictor for the division of pressure is screwed to the socket (Fig. 43) and can easily be replaced.

b) Torsion Restrictors

The torsion restrictors of the proportional-plus-reset and the proportional-plus-reset-plus-rate action restrictor blocks are soft sol-

dered with one end to the restrictor block socket and with the other
end to a coupling with hose connections (Fig. 43). Coupling and
drive mechanism correspond to the arrangement at the needle valve.
The index on the coupling sleeve which slides over a scale of the
dial face is bolted to the coupling sleeve when the torsion restrictor
is adjusted.

At the proportional-plus-reset restrictor block, the torsion restrictor
for the rate action is replaced by a fixed capillary tube soft soldered
at both ends to the socket (Fig. 43).

At the reset action restrictor block the upper connection of the torsion tube is open and the coupling sleeve is sealed from the column by
an "O" ring. Here, perhaps, small leaks are not critical, because on
this side of the restrictor there is enough output from the amplifier.

c) Zero Point Pressure Element in the Proportional Restrictor Block

For adjusting the zero point in the proportional restrictor block,
the normal precision pressure transmitter is used. It is fastened by
means of a clamping sleeve. The dial is firmly connected to the zero
point set screw.

d) Interconnection of Restrictor Elements

The air connections in the restrictor blocks are either formed by
holes in the sockets or by flexible connections in the torsion restrictors. The connections are plastic tubes (Fig. 46).

The significance of the socket connections is shown in Fig. 45.

5. Adjusting and Testing

Before being assembled into the restrictors, the restrictor elements
are carefully checked for perfect quality and especially for the
adequate adjustment range of their restricting effect. The manufacturing tolerances of the restrictor elements are so narrow that
individual calibration may be waived and preprinted dials may be
used. After assembly, the zero points of the dials are determined
by matching a definite restrictor mid-value and a corresponding
dial value. This position is fixed by bolting. Further checking of
other dial values confirms that the variations between the indicated
and the real restrictor values do not exceed the prescribed tolerances.

Assembly of the restrictor devices from simple and rugged elements offers high reliability in service. Disturbances can arise practically only from very dirty air. In such cases it is recommended replacing the whole restrictor block and this is easily done without interrupting the operation. The following method is recommended for checking the function of the restrictors.

a) Testing the Proportional Restrictors

For testing the proportional restrictors, a constant pressure is applied on the inlet of the pressure divider and the pressure between the fixed and adjustable restrictor is measured with a pressure gauge.

The setting up of a suitable test circuit is easily done according to Figs. 45 and 46.

At the proportional-plus-reset and the proportional-plus-reset-plus-rate action restrictor, compressed air of 1.2 kg/cm² is applied at port 1, and the pressure gauge is connected to port 2. Ports 3 and 4 are to be sealed.

The following values are adjusted with the needle valve, with the output pressures staying within the permissible limits:

Proportional Band Dial Value	Output Pressure
300%	1.20 — 0.02 kg/cm²
100%	0.40 ± 0.06 kg/cm²
10%	0.04 ± 0.02 kg/cm²

At the proportional controller the checking of the pressure divider is combined with that of the precision pressure transmitter. For that purpose, port 3 is connected with the air supply (1.4 kg/cm²) and port 2 with the pressure gauge. A pressure of 1.2 kg/cm² is ob-

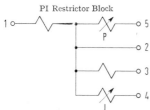

P Restrictor Block

I Restrictor Block

PI Restrictor Block

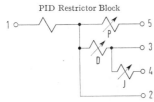

PID Restrictor Block

1 Amplifier Outlet
2 Negative Feedback (Inner Bellows)
3 Negative Feedback (Outer Bellows)
4 Positive Feedback
5 Atmosphere
6 Air Supply

Fig. 46

Restrictor Unit Circuits.

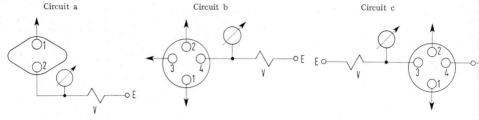

Circuit a   Circuit b   Circuit c

Circuit a-Test Circuit for I Restrictor in the I Restrictor Block   E   Connection for Inlet Pressure
Circuit b-Test Circuit for I Restrictor in the PI and PID Restrictor   V   Calibrated Reference Restrictor
        Block   ○⟶ Atmosphere Connection
Circuit c-Test Circuit for D Restrictor in the PID Restrictor Block   ○—⊣ Sealed Connection

Fig. 47   Restrictor Test Circuits.

tained with the zero point pressure element, port 1 being closed.
Then, port 1 is reopened. Then the following values are set by the
needle valve and the output pressures are compared to the permissible limits:

Proportional Band Dial Value	Output Pressure
300%	1.2 — 0.05 kg/cm²
100%	0.26 ± 0.02 kg/cm²
10%	0.04 ± 0.01 kg/cm²

b) Testing the Torsion Restrictors

Although the torsion restrictors are pure time elements, a pressure
dividing arrangement is used for testing them, too. By these means
the testing time can be considerably shortened because there is no
equalizing reaction. A calibrated comparison restrictor is used instead of the fixed restrictor, the former being of such proportions
that, together with a storage volume of 100 cm³, it produces a time
constant of one minute.

The testing circuits for testing the torsion restrictors in the reset,
proportional-plus-reset and proportional-plus-reset-plus-rate action
restrictor blocks are shown in Fig. 47.

The input pressure (port E) is set to 0.5 kg/cm². Linked pairs of
values of the dial and of the pressure for the pressure divider arrangements are as follows for the different types of restrictor blocks:

	Dial Value	Output Pressure kg/cm²
Reset action restrictor in the reset action restrictor block	2	< 0.04
	60	0.33 to 0.36
	600	> 0.46
Reset action restrictor in the proportional-plus-reset and the proportional-plus-reset-plus-rate action restrictor block	0.1	< 0.06
	1	0.24 to 0.27
	30	> 0.47
Rate action restrictor in the proportional-plus-reset-plus-rate action restrictor block	0.05	< 0.06
	1	0.32 to 0.35
	15	> 0.45

6. TECHNICAL DATA

Proportional action restrictor:

Input restriction

    Proportional controller . . . . 0.3 mm dia.

    Proportional-plus-reset and proportional-plus-reset-plus-rate action controller . . . . . . 0.38 mm dia.

Needle valve . . . . 1.5 mm dia.

    Plug cone. . . . . 1 : 30

    Plug travel . . . . 6 mm

Adjustment ranges:

> Proportional band range for proportional-plus-
> reset and for proportional-plus-reset-plus-
> rate action controllers . . . . 10 to 300%
>
> Proportional band range for proportional con-
> troller . . . . 5 to 300%

Torsion restrictor:
> Turning angle . . . . maximum 80°

Adjustment ranges:

> Reset action restrictor in the reset action
> restrictor block . . . . 2 to 600 sec
>
> Reset action restrictor in the proportional-
> plus-reset and in the proportional-plus-reset-
> plus-rate action restrictor block . . . . . 0.1 to 30 min
>
> Rate action restrictor . . . . 0.05 to 15 min

E. Short Circuiting Relay

In fast controlled systems it has been found expedient to install the
controllers directly at the final control element, instead of in the
control room. By these means the interconnection between controller output and final control element can be kept as short as possible, thus avoiding the lags in long actuating lines. Naturally,
manual control of the final control element from the control room
will not be given up. The necessary switch equipment for this purpose is the short circuiting relay. Flow controllers are equipped
with it and so are the proportional-plus-reset and the proportional-
plus-reset-plus-rate action controllers when they are locally mounted. The short circuiting relay receives the necessary signals for a
switchover through activating the switch in the control station.

1. Principle and Mode of Operation

Fig. 48 shows a schematic cross-section through the short circuiting
relay with the two possible switch positions. In the "AUTOMATIC"

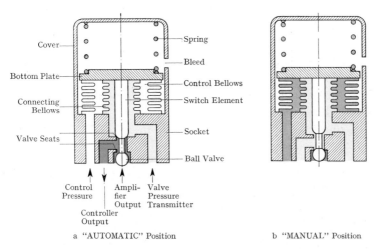

Fig. 48   Design and Switch Positions of the Short Circuit Relay.

position of the control station, the control pressure is equal to atmospheric pressure. The relay is in the switch position as shown in Fig. 48a, where amplifier output and controller output are interconnected. In the "MANUAL" position, however, the relay receives a control pressure from the control station equal to the supply pressure (1.4 kg/cm²). The relay is in the switch position as indicated in Fig. 48b, where manual actuating pressure is connected to the diaphragm motor and the feedback bellows of the controller. The switch pressure acts against a pre-compressed spring through the control bellows. If the switch pressure is greater than 0.7 kg/cm², the switch element of the short circuiting relay is pushed from the position as shown in Fig. 48a to the position as shown in Fig. 48b.

2. Design

The short circuiting relay is a pneumatic three-way cock. The switch element (Figs. 48 and 50) is firmly connected to the control bellows. The inner bellows acts as a seal. A prestressed spring pushes the valve into one of its two switch positions (Fig. 48a) as long as the control bellows has no pressure. The connection with the socket is through the cover screwed on top. The four connections for amplifier outlet pressure, valve positioning pressure, control pressure of the control station, and output of the short circuit relay terminate as holes in the socket base plate and are sealed to the controller base plate with "O" rings (Fig. 49).

The individual parts from which the device is assembled are shown in Fig. 50. The double bellows system is soldered pressure-tight to the bottom plate and the socket.

The short circuiting relay is built as a plug-in unit. The correspond-

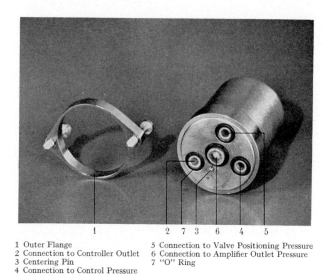

1 Outer Flange	5 Connection to Valve Positioning Pressure
2 Connection to Controller Outlet	6 Connection to Amplifier Outlet Pressure
3 Centering Pin	7 "O" Ring
4 Connection to Control Pressure	

Fig. 49   Short Circuit Relay with Cap Flange.

ing base plate contains the counterbores and a guide for the centering pin, which insures correct assembly in the right position. The relay is held in place by an outer flange pulled down against the chassis plate by two screws (Fig. 49).

3. Adjusting and Testing

As the short circuit relay is a simple pneumatic switch, adjustment can be limited to setting the switch point and the switch travel. Because the switch signals are 0 or 1.4 kg/cm², the switch point is set to about 0.7 kg/cm² in order to have the same switching power in both switch positions. The amount of switch element travel between both end positions of the switch must be great enough so that the opened valve position provides sufficient cross section for a large controller outlet air flow. On the other hand, the switch travel should not exceed the required amount so that the life of the bellows will not be shortened through over-expansion. The optimum switch travel is about 1 mm.

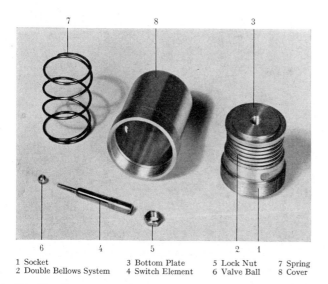

| 1 Socket | 3 Bottom Plate | 5 Lock Nut | 7 Spring |
| 2 Double Bellows System | 4 Switch Element | 6 Valve Ball | 8 Cover |

Fig. 50   Components of the Short Circuit Relay.

a) Adjusting the Switch Point

The switch point is adjusted by prestressing the spring through changing the screw length of the switch element in the bottom of the bellows. With the cover off, the switch element is turned until the upper valve seat is just cleared. Then the jam nut is tightened and the thread sealed with lacquer.

b) Adjusting the Switch Travel

The valve ball is screwed so far on the switch element, until the desired switch travel results. The switch travel is correctly adjusted when the bellows plate can be moved approximately 1 mm towards the spring.

c) Testing

The tightness and the maximum air flow in both switch positions are checked by means of a flowmeter. The control pressures are 0 and 1.4 kg/cm². The leakage with the valve closed may not exceed 0.2 Std. l/min. With the valve opened, on the other hand, the air flow must be 50 Std. l/min. For this purpose, compressed air at 1.0 kg/cm² is applied at the outlet pressure port through a suitable flowmeter. According to the switch position, the connections for outlet pressure and valve positioning pressure must be closed, (tightness test) or opened (maximum flow test). The short circuiting relay socket connections are shown in Fig. 49.

The switch point can be determined at the flowmeter as well, since the throttling at the valve seat immediately changes when the switch element moves. This switch point should exist between control pressures of 0.6 to 0.8 kg/cm². If necessary, the switch point must be readjusted accordingly.

4. Sources of Error

Since the short circuiting relay requires no specific measuring properties, failures very seldom occur beforehand. Only leakages come into question. They may be caused by mechanical damages or cloggings. With the recommended test, faults are easily detected and corrected. Special maintenance is not required.

5. Technical Data

Outer diameter	40 mm
Mounting surface when fastening with outer flange	40 mm × 40 mm
Over-all size	55 mm
Weight	250 g
Medium switch pressure	0.7 kg/cm²
Maximum switch pressure	2.0 kg/cm²
Switch travel	1 mm
Leak rate per seat	$\leqq$ 0.2 Std. l/min
Maximum air flow per seat	80 Std. l/min

F. Input Pressure Controller

If the accuracy requirements of the pneumatic and electropneumatic instruments are particularly high, the fixed restrictor of the pilot control can be replaced by an input pressure controller. The instruments thus become insensitive even to very large deviations in supply pressure.

1. PRINCIPLE AND DESIGN

The input pressure controller is a direct working proportional controller (Fig. 51). The set point for the controlled pressure is set by a

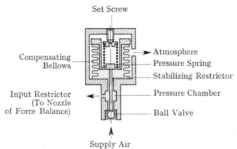

Set Screw

Compensating Bellows

Atmosphere
Pressure Spring
Stabilizing Restrictor

Input Restrictor (To Nozzle of Force Balance)

Pressure Chamber

Ball Valve

Supply Air

Fig. 51   Input Pressure Controller Schematic.

compressed spring. The controlled pressure acts against the spring force through a bellows. If the controlled pressure does not correspond to its set point, the air is throttled by means of a ball seat valve until force equilibrium is again established. For purposes of stability, the controlled pressure has a delayed effect on the bellows caused by a restriction.

The controlled pressure is 1.1 kg/cm^2 and is fed via the input restrictor represented by a hole to the pressure chamber to the nozzle. The input pressure controller is installed in the appropriate instruments. The two air connections are sealed by "O" rings (Fig. 52).

2. ADJUSTING AND TESTING

The tightness of the compensating bellows and the perfect seating of the ball valve are to be checked. The set point is adjusted by compressing the pressure spring with the threaded pin.

1 Input Pressure Controller, Assembled   3 Cover   5 Pressure Spring
2 Plug   4 Threaded Pin   6 Spring Plate

Fig. 52   Input Pressure Controller.

Adjusting and testing are done according to the circuit shown in Fig. 53. For this purpose, the input pressure controller is plugged into a test base with hose connections and is held in place by a clamping frame.

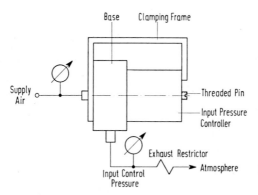

Fig. 53   Adjusting and Testing Circuit.

The supply pressure is set to $1.4 \, kg/cm^2$ and the input control pressure is adjusted to $0.6 \, kg/cm^2$ with the threaded pin. If the supply pressure changes by $0.2 \, kg/cm^2$, the maximum input control pressure change may be $\pm 0.02 \, kg/cm^2$.

3. TECHNICAL DATA

Input restrictor hole . . . . 0.65 mm dia.

Allowable supply pressure . . . . 2 kg/cm²

Controlled pressure . . . . 1.1 kg/cm²

Air flow within the control range . . . . 5 Std.l/min

III. PNEUMATIC INSTRUMENTS

A. Pneumatic Proportional-Plus-Reset Action and Proportional-Plus-Reset-Plus-Rate Action Controllers

1. Special Characteristics

The pneumatic proportional-plus-reset and the proportional-plus-reset-plus-rate action controllers (Fig. 54) are "plug-in" controllers, which are usually plugged into the rear of the recorders (Fig. 55). They are marked by the following special features:

The results of the modular construction allow not only for easy interchangeability of component parts, but also allow the proportional-plus-reset action controller to be expanded to a proportional-plus-reset-plus-rate action controller by exchanging the restrictor unit. The exchange of components can be made as well in a controller

Fig. 54 TELEPNEU PI (PID) Controller.

already installed. After switching to manual operation and disconnecting the controller by means of a switch on the connecting plate, the components can be easily replaced even in operation without disturbing the plant.

TELEPNEU controllers possess progressive action and put out an increasing air flow with increases in measured variable deviation. Because of this feature, the controllers are largely insensitive to noise level, to self-induced oscillations, and to changes in the dynamic behavior of the control loop caused by load changes. The special design of the amplifier based on the principle of low air consumption makes it possible to operate the controllers with very low air consumption. This means high operating efficiency in large plants.

High control accuracy, even with widely deviating air supply pressures, is insured by a special pressure controller for the pilot control (input pressure controller). With a stable air supply it can always be replaced by a fixed input restrictor.

1 Control Station   2 Recorder   3 Plug-In Controller

Fig. 55 Pneumatic Controller Unit Consisting of Pneumatic Plug-In Controller, Recorder, and Control Station.

2. Principle and Mode of Operation

a) Measuring and Amplifying the Control Deviation

The controllers work on the principle of force balance.

The forces produced by the set point, measured value, and feedback bellows create a resulting moment about the fulcrum at the force balance beam. When control deviations occur, this moment causes the beam to deflect from the zero position.

Such a deflection of the beam changes the throttling of the air between nozzle and flapper, whereby a change in pressure is produced between the fixed input restrictor and the nozzle. This pressure change affects the input to the amplifier and, thereby, is amplified 20-fold. If the supply pressure oscillates, the input pressure controller holds the pressure constant at the input restrictor. By the mutual effect of force balance and amplifier, the controller amplifies control deviations 400-fold, corresponding to a smallest proportional band setting of 0.25%.

b) Adjusting the Proportional Band

In order to change the proportional band, the amplifier outlet pressure is fed to the feedback bellows through an air pressure dividing arrangement. By changing the adjustable restrictor (needle valve of both the proportional-plus-reset action and the proportional-plus-reset-plus-rate action restrictor block), the influence of the amplifier output pressure on the feedback can be regulated. This permits arbitrary adjustment of the controller proportional band between the minimum value of 0.25% and the maximum value of 300%, which is given by the geometry of the force balance.

c) Structure of the Transient Behavior

The proportional-plus-reset-action controller is provided with an elastic feedback (Fig. 56). For this purpose, the pressure in the negative feedback bellows is connected to the positive feedback bellows across an adjustable torsion restrictor, the I restrictor, and a volume. This +R bellows is attached at the same distance from the pivot, but on the other side of the force balance. Consequently, the effect of the —R bellows is counteracted according to the time adjusted at the reset action restrictor for each proportional band. This proportional response has only a passing effect. After

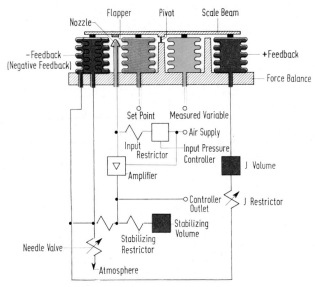

Fig. 56　PI Controller Circuit Diagram.

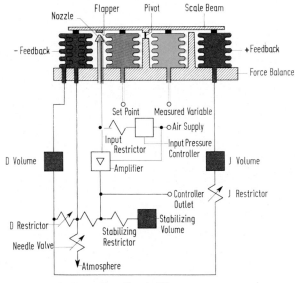

Fig. 57　PID Controller Circuit Diagram.

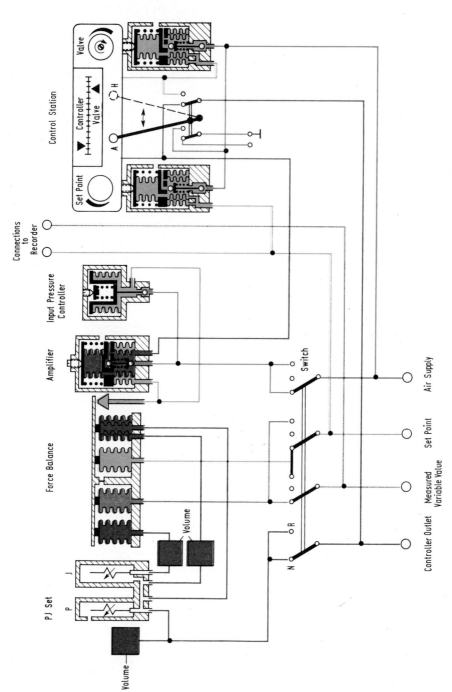

Fig. 58   Circuit Diagram of the Board Mounted PI Controller with Standard Control Station.

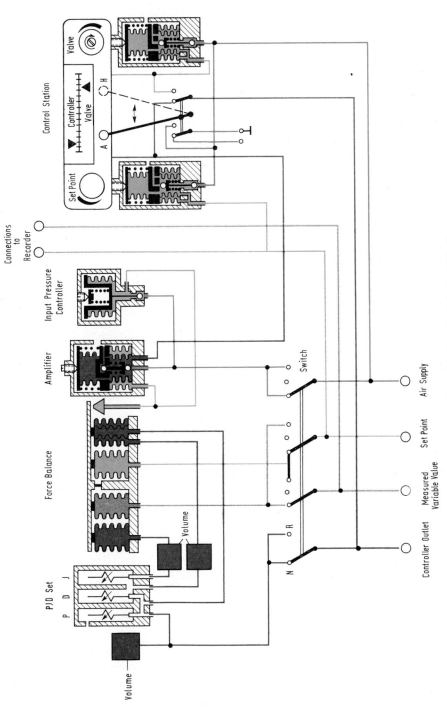

Fig. 59 Circuit Diagram of the Board Mounted PID Controller with Standard Control Station.

the lapse of reset action time, the minimum proportional band value, "the constant proportional band", is obtained. This corresponds to the highest pressure amplification and amounts to approximately 0.25%. The inherent stability is guaranteed even without a damping capacity connected outside of the controller by a stabilizing capacity within.

With the proportional-plus-reset-plus-rate action controller there is a lag in the feedback pressure, too. This is done by another torsion restrictor, the rate action restrictor, and a capacity. Thus, the feedback works submissively and delaying (Fig. 57). The controller temporarily achieves an amplification greater than the proportional band setting would correspond to.

For reasons of control dynamics, it is sensible to limit the rate action effect. This is done by the inner bellows of the +R feedback on which the effect of the amplifier is not delayed (five-bellows force balance).

d) Positioning Speed and Dynamic Actuating Range

The special feature of the TELEPNEU controller is the great output amplification and the corresponding high positioning speed obtained. The output air flow is controlled within a certain range by the deviation (progressive control). The dynamic actuating range amounts to approximately four percent of the inlet pressure range.

Figs. 58 and 59 show the circuits of both complete proportional-plus-reset and proportional-plus-reset-plus-rate action controllers, consisting of controller base plate and connecting plate. The switch at the controller connecting plate has three positions: In the N position ("NORMAL"), an increasing measured variable value causes increasing outlet pressure. In the R position ("REVERSED"), an increasing measured variable value causes decreasing outlet pressure. In the middle position, all connections between the connection plate and the base plate (the actual controller) are broken, permitting interchanging of component parts.

3. DESIGN AND ASSEMBLY

The complete plug-in controller consists of the actual controlling device; i.e. of the controller base plate with all component units and the controller connection plate.

The controller base plate is screwed to the connecting plate. The sealing of the five air connections is done with "O" rings which are inserted into the base plate. In the controller base plate are the volumes shown in Figures 56 and 57 (integral action, derivative action, and stabilizing volumes). These are near to the connecting lines for the individual components. The complete proportional-plus-reset and the proportional-plus-reset-plus-rate action controllers have a total of 13 air connections. On the rear, there are eight

1 Pneumatic Force Balance
2 PID Restrictor Block
3 Input Pressure Controller
4 Controller Base
5 Hold-Down Screws
6 Pneumatic Amplifier
7 Controller Connecting Plate
8 Switch
9 Supply Air Connection
10 Controller Outlet
11 Measured Variable Connection

Fig. 60   TELEPNEU PID Controller;
Cover Removed.

plug-in connections for joining with the recorder and the control station (Fig. 61). The compression fittings on the front side are for connecting the controller to the supply air and the controlled system. On the controller connecting plate is the manual switch for reversing the direction of the controller effect. In the switch mid-position shown in Fig. 60, the five connections between the connecting plate and the base plate are broken.

In order to mount the controller to the recorder, its protecting cover is removed after loosening a knurled screw. Then, the three hold-down screws of the base plate (Fig. 60) are loosened so that the base plate can be removed. The controller connecting plate is plugged into the recorder. The control station or the multiplying relay is plugged in and then it is fastened to the controller with two screws. Finally, the controller base plate is again screwed to the connecting plate.

4. Types and Possibilities of Application

The Telepneu proportional-plus-reset action and the proportional-plus-reset-plus-rate action controllers are applicable principally to all types of control in the processing industry. Flow control of com-

1 Input Pressure Controller Cover Plate
2 Controller Connection Panel
3 Cover
4 Plug-In Connections to Recorder
5 Plug-In Connections to Control Station

Fig. 61   Plug Connections at Rear of the
PI and PID Controller.

pressible media and pressure control of plants with surge capacities have always had satisfactory results when proportional-plus-reset action controllers are employed. With particularly long lags or distance velocity lags of the controlled systems, as found in many temperature controlled systems, better results are provided by proportional-plus-reset-plus-rate action controllers.

The controllers are mostly foreseen for mounting on the rear of the controllers in the control room (Fig. 55). A special design offering a differently constructed connecting plate and short circuiting relay permits local mounting of the controller with remote switching in the control room from "MANUAL" to "AUTOMATIC" operation. This corresponds to the arrangement of the Telepneu flow controller for valve mounting. According to the type of restrictor block, the controller functions as a proportional-plus-reset action or as a proportional-plus-reset-plus-rate action controller. A proportional-plus-reset action controller may be expanded to a proportional-plus-reset-plus-rate action controller by simply exchanging the restrictor block. After screwing off the protective cap, the adjusting screws for proportional band, rate time, and reset time can be turned with a screwdriver (Fig. 60).

The values for proportional, reset, and rate action are continuously adjustable within the following ranges:

P (proportional action) from 10 to 300%,
I (reset action) from 0.1 to 30 minutes (time constant),
D (rate action) from 0.05 to 15 minutes (time constant).

5. ADJUSTING AND TESTING

The proportional-plus-reset action and proportional-plus-reset-plus-rate action controllers are tested and adjusted units. Testing before putting them into operation is not necessary. The building block components—pneumatic force balance, input pressure controller, restrictor block, amplifier, controller connecting plate, controller base plate—are tested before assembly according to the adjustment and calibration instructions. The test tolerances of individual parts are so fixed that readjustment after assembly is not required.

If faulty operation of the controller is suspected, testing and adjusting should be done in accordance with the following:

Check all plug-in connections for tightness and check control accuracy over the entire control range.

Test the zero point of the controller. It is characterized by the fact that there is no difference between set point and measured variable value when the operating mode is reversed and with a set point value of 0.6 kg/cm².

For adjusting and testing, the controller is plugged into a tested recorder and a tested control station as shown in Fig. 55. Flexible tubes are connected to the four Ermeto fittings, making up the test schematic shown in Fig. 62.

The controller outlet pressure goes to the measured variable connection (short circuit). This provides a simple control loop. The controller accuracy can be readily controlled by measuring the difference between set point and measured variable. For this a water-filled U-tube manometer can be used as a differential pressure gauge.

The controller switch is moved to the "R" position and the manual-automatic switch of the control station is moved to the "AUTOMATIC" position. With the proportional-plus-reset-plus-rate action

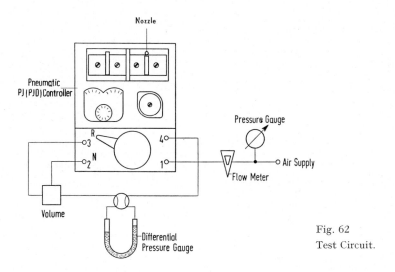

Fig. 62
Test Circuit.

controller, set $I = 0$, $D = 0$ and $P = 300\%$. With the proportional-plus-reset action controller, set $I = 0$ and $P = 300\%$. The switch at the differential pressure gauge isolates the pressure gauge from the two pressures.

a) Tightness Test

Set the supply pressure to 1.4 kg/cm². Adjust the set point to 1.0 kg/cm² (100%). The air consumption measured with the flow-meter may not exceed 9 Std.l/min.

b) Adjusting the Zero Point

Wait until the difference between the measured value and the set point is less than 0.03 kg/cm². If required, readjust the nozzle at the force balance. Switch in the differential pressure gauge and readjust the nozzle so that the difference in pressure on the differential pressure gauge does not exceed 10 mm of water.

c) Testing the Control Accuracy throughout the Range

Slowly decrease the set point value to $0.2\ kg/cm^2$ (0%). The remaining difference in pressure on the differential pressure gauge may not exceed 40 mm of water.

6. Sources of Error and their Repair

Failures can be caused by cloggings, leakages, or mechanical damages.

If faulty performance is noticed in a proportional-plus-reset action or a proportional-plus-reset-plus-rate action controller and no large leaks are detected in the plug-in connections to recorder and control station (or multiplying relay), there is a failure in the control device. Then the plug-in units of the force balance, input pressure controller, amplifier, and restrictor block are individually tested or replaced one after the other by tested units. Thus, the failure may be identified as belonging to a certain component. Special maintenance is not required.

7. Adjusting and Putting the Control System into Operation

If the installation of a control system having TELEPNEU components has been carefully done, there should be no difficulties experienced when the system is put into operation. This applies especially to the cleanness of the air supply and the tightness of all pipe connections. Usually, when starting up a control system, it is recommended to manually position the actuator in order to bring the final control element into a position corresponding to the desired value of the measured variable. Thus, it is easy to determine whether or not the adjusted controller operating mode corresponds to the controlled system. If increasing control pressure causes increasing measured variable value, then the switch on the control station must be moved to the "R" position. If increasing control pressure causes decreasing measured variable value, the switch is moved to the "N" position. The principle of progressive closed loop control has the decisive advantage that at start up it is easy to adapt the controller to the controlled system. When the controller parameters only approximate the optimum values, the operation may be switched from "MANUAL" to "AUTOMATIC" without any further considerations.

At the time when the final control element is hand actuated, it is easy to recognize how the control parameters are to be adjusted. If small changes in manual control pressure cause large changes of the controlled variable, a larger proportional band value will be required. If the controlled variable quickly follows a change in manual control pressure, then small rate action and reset action values must be chosen. If the conditions are reversed, long times will give more favorable results. Naturally, the more exact optimization of the control system can only be established with automatic control. In this case, it must be first decided whether the controller will be tuned predominantly for load disturbances or set point changes. In both cases, the progressive behavior has been found to be a great help in quickly finding the optimum control parameters. As a general indication, it can be pointed out that the proportional band setting as well as the reset time have to be increased if the control loop tends to oscillate.

As already mentioned, the proportional band in Telepneu controllers is adjusted pneumatically by means of a pressure dividing circuit. This method offers the advantage that the force balance system is extraordinarily accurate and, at the same time, is rugged and dependable in operation.

It may be thought that when the proportional band setting is changed in operation unintended control reactions will be caused. However, this is not likely to cause trouble as changes in proportional band setting are only made while putting the controller into operation and then, only step by step. A complete bumpless shift in the proportional band setting is possible if a switchover to manual operation is carried out beforehand.

8. Technical Data

Dimensions . . . . 200 mm × 185 mm × 136 mm

Weight . . . . 5 kg

Adjustable proportional band . . . . 10 to 300%

Adjustable reset time . . . . 0.1 to 30 minutes

Adjustable rate time . . . . 0.05 to 15 minutes

Actuating range 0.3%

Sustained deviation with a
   300% proportional band 0.2%

Hysteresis 0.1%

Sensitivity 0.01%

Average air consumption . . . . . . 5 Std. l/min

Maximum outlet air flow . . . . . . 50 Std. l/min

Supply pressure error with input pres-
   sure controller . . . . <0.1%/0.1 kg/cm² of
                                     supply pressure change

Supply pressure error without input
   pressure controller . . . . 0.4%/0.1 kg/cm² of
                                     supply pressure change

B. Flow and Level Controllers

In process industry plants, especially in continuous processes, the control of flow and liquid level are of special significance. Troublefree operating performance depends on them and they make up the majority of the controllers. Naturally, it is always possible to solve control problems with proportional-plus-reset action or with proportional-plus-reset-plus-rate action controllers. But in order to meet the special requirements of these controls still better, it is appropriate to use special controllers which, in the TELEPNEU system, may be assembled from the existing components.

Flow control mostly involves very fast controlled system problems. The controller, therefore, is installed at the final control element in order to make the control loop as short as possible. For reasons of control dynamics, this controller has fixed proportional band and adjustable reset time.

Since in level control the level often has to change with the load, proportional action controllers are preferred to proportional-plus-reset action controllers. It is advantageous if every desired controller output pressure can be achieved for every set point value and for every adjusted proportional band range. Therefore, both a parallel shift of the characteristics and a rotation about an average intersection point must be possible.

1. THE PNEUMATIC FLOW CONTROLLER

a) Mode of Operation

The mode of operation of the flow controller (Fig. 63) is in principle very similar to that of the proportional-plus-reset action controller. Since the controller has a fixed proportional band range, the adjustable proportional action restrictor is not required. Fig. 64 shows the unit schematically.

The amplifier output pressure is fed to the feedback through the short circuit relay and a stabilizing volume. First of all, the effective controller pressure amplification is thus limited to $\frac{1}{3}$ which corresponds to a proportional band of 300%. The reset action effect is produced by feeding the feedback pressure through an adjustable

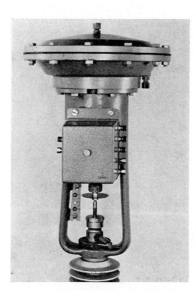

torsion restrictor (the reset action restrictor) to a bellows located on the opposite side of the force balance and at an equal distance from the counter-linkage bellows as the feedback bellows. Thus, the feedback effect of the counter-linkage corresponding to the reset time adjusted at the reset action restrictor is again neutralized.

The stabilizing volume between the short circuit relay and the feedback insures self-stability of the controller even when no volume is attached to the controller output. The amplifier output pressure is indicated in the usual manner on the pressure gauge of

Fig. 63   Flow Controller Mounted on the Final Control Element.

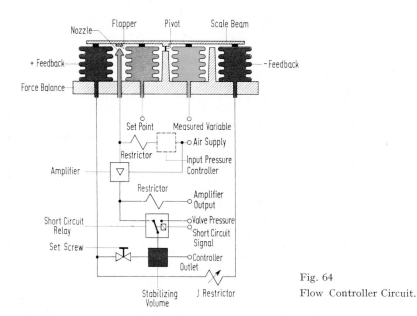

Fig. 64
Flow Controller Circuit.

the control station located in the control room. In order not to adversely affect the control velocity because of the volume of the line, this line is connected across a restrictor.

In the "AUTOMATIC" position, the amplifier output pressure goes to the final control element through the short circuit relay; in the "MANUAL" position, the valve pressure transmitter output similarly goes this route. In this case, the control station switch just furnishes the switch impulses for the short circuit relay.

With manual operation, the set screw between the stabilizing volume and feedback allows interchange of all components up to the short circuit relay.

In all other respects the controller possesses the qualities already known about proportional-plus-reset action and proportional-plus-reset-plus-rate action controllers. These provide a high degree of accuracy, a large output air flow with very small air consumption and progressive response of the final control element.

b) Design and Assembly

The components consist of a four-bellows force balance, amplifier, reset action restrictor, short circuit relay, and input pressure re-

1 Base
2 Four-Bellows Force Balance
3 Pneumatic Amplifier
4 I Restrictor
5 Short Circuit Relay
6 Input Restrictor
7 Compression Fittings (Ermeto Type)

Fig. 65
Flow Controller with
Cover Removed.

strictor (or input pressure controller). These are mounted on a base plate containing a distributor and stabilizer volume of about 100 cm³ (Fig. 65). The components mounted on the base plate are covered by a cast iron cap. The controller is attached to the final control element with two screws.

The pressure lines are connected to Ermeto compression fittings (Fig. 65). To reverse the controller action, set point and measured variable connections are interchanged.

c) Range of Application

The controller is installed in fast controlled systems; e.g., for controlling the flow of incompressible fluids or pressure systems without storage capacities. In addition, it can be used in all cases where single knob adjustment (reset action time) can satisfy the conditions of the control technique. The reset time may be continuously adjusted at the reset action restrictor block within an approximate range of 2 to 600 seconds.

d) Testing and Adjusting

Adjustment of the controller is not required because, as is the case with all TELEPNEU instruments, it consists only of tested and adjusted components. Testing the instrument involves checking its function. This can be repeated at any time using simple means. Things to be checked are the tightness of all plug-in connections, control accuracy over the entire control range, and the short circuit mechanism.

For testing purposes, the controller is connected to an arrangement as shown in Fig. 66. A water-filled U-tube manometer best serves as a differential pressure gauge.

As is the case with the proportional-plus-reset action and with the proportional-plus-reset-plus-rate action controllers, the test arrangement is a control circuit whereby control accuracy throughout the entire range is checked by changing the set point value. The flow of air indicated at the flowmeter may not amount to more than 9 Std.l/min since it represents a measure of the tightness of the plug-in connections.

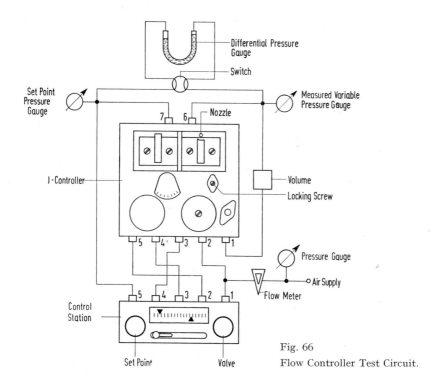

Fig. 66

Flow Controller Test Circuit.

The short circuit relay functioning is tested with the differential pressure gauge disconnected. The manual control pressure is set to 0.6 kg/cm² and, in the "MANUAL" switch position, the measured variable pressure gauge must also read 0.6 kg/cm².

With the aid of this test method, the reasons for errors are easily recognized and may be eliminated by replacing the components in question.

e) Adjusting and Putting the Control System into Operation

The same aspects apply to putting a flow controller into operation as for the controllers mounted in the control room (proportional-plus-reset action and proportional-plus-reset-plus-rate action controllers). Adapting to the controlled system is particularly easy since only one parameter exists. The reset time is simply increased until stable control is established.

f) Technical Data

Weight	3.0 kg
Adjustable reset time	2 to 600 seconds
Actuating range	0.2%
Hysteresis	0.1%
Sensitivity	0.01%
Average air consumption	5 Std. l/min
Maximum output air flow	50 Std. l/min
Supply pressure error without input pressure controller	0.2%/0.1 kg/cm² of supply pressure change
Supply pressure error with input pressure controller	$<0.1\%$/0.1 kg/cm² of supply pressure change

2. THE PNEUMATIC PROPORTIONAL CONTROLLER

a) Mode of Operation

The special functions of proportional control require a controller whose amplification and zero point must be adjustable over the

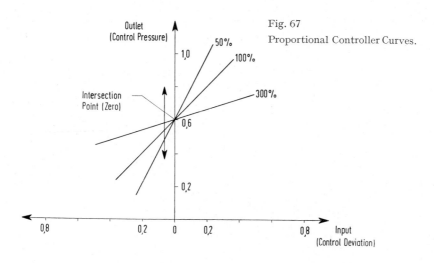

Fig. 67
Proportional Controller Curves.

widest limits (Fig. 67). That means that the characteristic curves of the controller (proportional band) have to be rotated around a common intersection. The intersection of the characteristic curves (zero point of the controller) has to be movable over the entire control pressure range. The technical accomplishment for rotating the characteristic curves is done with a pressure dividing arrangement having one fixed and one adjustable restrictor, as with proportional-plus-reset action and with proportional-plus-reset-plus-rate action controllers. The intersection of the characteristic curves is determined by the counter pressure of the pressure dividing arrangement (Fig. 68). With proportional-plus-reset action and with proportional-plus-reset-plus-rate action controllers this counter pressure is always

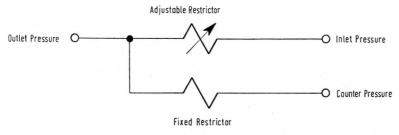

Fig. 68   Circuit of the Pneumatic Pressure Divider Circuit.

atmospheric pressure. Contrariwise, with the proportional action controller it is determined by a pressure element built into the restrictor block.

The circuit of the proportional action controller is shown in Fig. 69. To achieve the adjustable proportional band, the amplifier output pressure is fed directly to the negative feedback bellows and indirectly to the positive feedback bellows by way of the pressure divider. The positive feedback bellows is connected to the zero point

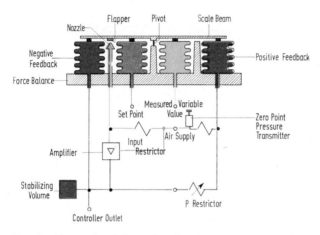

Fig. 69   Proportional Controller Circuit Diagram.

pressure transmitter through the fixed restrictor of the pressure divider network. If the adjustable restrictor of the pressure divider (proportional action restriction) is closed, the amplifier output pressure affects only the negative feedback bellows and, thus, creates the maximum proportional band of 300%. The level at the positive feedback bellows adjusted by the zero point pressure element remains unchanged.

If the proportional action restrictor is opened, the amplifier output pressure partly affects the positive feedback bellows, too, and thus decreases the proportional band. With a fully opened proportional action restrictor, the same pressure exists in both feedback bellows and, thus, the feedback has no effect whatsoever and the controller has its smallest proportional band.

The self-stability of the controller is insured by a built-in stabilizing volume and is not a function of any external damping capacity connected to the controller.

b) Design and Assembly

The TELEPNEU proportional action controller (Fig. 70) is normally a plug-in controller, like the proportional-plus-reset action and the proportional-plus-reset-plus-rate action controllers. In its de-

1 Four-Bellows Force
  Balance
2 P Restrictor Block
3 Amplifier
4 Controller Base Plate

Fig. 70
Proportional Controller Assembly.

sign, the proportional action controller differs but little from the other plug-in controllers. The five-bellows force balance is replaced by a four-bellows force balance and, besides the proportional band restrictor, the restrictor block contains a precision pressure transmitter for the controller zero point. The input pressure controller is not necessary because a fixed input pressure restrictor fulfills all accuracy requirements.

Naturally, the controller base plate is so designed that the same connecting plate used with the rest of the plug-in controllers may be used.

c) Types

The proportional action controller is used where load or set point dependent deviations cause no disturbance or are even desired.

The controller is particularly meant for control room mounting as a plug-in controller. A special type controller connecting plate furnished with short circuit relay allows local mounting in the plant for remote operation from "MANUAL" to "AUTOMATIC" by a control station located in the control room. The proportional band

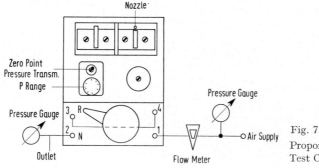

Fig. 71
Proportional Controller
Test Circuit.

of the controller can be continuously adjusted from 5 to 300%, and the zero point in the range of 0.2 to 1.0 kg/cm². Adjusting is done with a screwdriver after taking off the protective cover.

d) Adjusting and Testing

As shown in the circuit in Fig. 71, the controller is checked for leaks and function in its normal combination with recorder and control station. With the control station in its automatic position, the air consumption shall not exceed 6 Std.1/min.

If the controller zero point is correctly adjusted, and with equal pressures in the set point and measured variable bellows, a change in the proportional action restrictor causes no change in amplifier output pressure. Testing and necessary readjusting are done as follows:

The set point pressure element of the control station may be set to any value since equal values between set point and measured variable are always guaranteed by the short circuit in the test arrangement. The proportional action restrictor is adjusted to 300% and amplifier output pressure is brought to 0.6 kg/cm² with the aid of the pressure element in the restrictor block. If this output pressure changes when running through the entire proportional band range from 300 to 5%, this change can be voided by turning the nozzle on the force balance.

e) Adjusting and Putting Into Operation

In addition to those for the other controllers, there are some new aspects to be observed when adjusting and putting the proportional action controller into operation. Contrary to what is customary, the proportional band is not only changed for stabilizing a control but often has to be frequently adjusted according to technical and operational plant considerations. Since the aim of level control is often to utilize the storage effect of vessels, the adjusted proportional band has to be in a certain ratio to the storage capacity according to the operational flow variations.

f) Technical Data

Length	162 mm
Width	162 mm
Height	131 mm
Weight	3.0 kg
Adjustable proportional band	5 to 300%
Adjustable zero point	0.2 to 1.0 kg/cm²
Actuating range	0.25%
Zero point change by changing the proportional band	0.3%
Hysteresis	0.1%
Sensitivity	0.01%
Supply pressure error	<0.1%/0.1 kg/cm² of supply pressure change
Air consumption	3.5 Std.l/min
Maximum output air flow	50 Std.l/min

C. Pneumatic Positioners

1. FUNCTIONS AND SUMMARY

Positioners are provided for three very important functions:

a) Position Control

In slow controlled systems (temperature controls), for purposes of good control it is extremely important that the position of the actuator always be in strict accordance with the output pressure of the controller. Errors in position, for example, caused by friction and slack or by reverse actions in the sensing medium will cause lasting deviations, which must be regulated in the slow controlled system. In this case a positioner is used as a position controller. All deviations occurring between position demanded by the controller and the actual position are now immediately eliminated and, therefore, no longer have a disturbing effect on the main controlled variable. The output pressure of the controller is now the set point for this downstream position controller, acting here as an example of cascade control.

b) Increase of Positioning Speed

Long signal lines between controller and positioning motor cause a decrease in positioning speed because of the throttle effect of the lines and the storage effect of the positioning motor. This is especially undesirable in fast controlled systems because, as a result, fast disturbances cannot be sufficiently removed. To improve the quality of control, an output amplifier with low input volume is included in the positioning motor. Generally, a positioner is used for this purpose which, in addition to the output amplifier, takes care of a position control. However, a normal proportional action positioner is hardly suitable for this special function because, as a consequence of its unfavorable transient behavior, it can cause an instability of control in fast controlled systems. Therefore, here proportional and reset action in the positioner are necessary.

c) Several Final Control Elements in Relieving Operation

In many processing situations, two or more final control elements in series and relieving each other must be actuated by the same controller. A well-known example is the temperature control with separate heating and cooling devices. Here the total control pressure range of the controller is so distributed between the two final control elements that these react to different ranges of the control pressure. When positioners are used, this problem can be solved as well with normal positioning motors. To that end, the desired ratios between command pressure ranges and the stroke have only to be set by adjusting the linkages.

The positioners are always mounted on the actuating motor (Fig. 72). The following types of actuating motors and positioners are designed for the purpose in question:

Spring-released actuators contain only one pressure chamber. Accordingly, "single-acting" positioners are employed here.

Springless diaphragm motors have two actuating pressure chambers just like piston motors. For that reason, the "double-acting" positioners designed for them operate with two amplifiers controlled in opposite directions.

In many cases, such a large air output is required in a single-acting positioner that one amplifier is not sufficient. In this exceptional case, the so-called power positioner is employed. It contains a second amplifier connected in parallel.

2. PRINCIPLE AND OPERATION

Fig. 72
TELEPNEU Positioner Mounted on a Diaphragm Valve.

The TELEPNEU positioners operate uniformly in accordance with the principle of force balance. Circuit and operation of the different types are as follows:

a) The Single-Acting Positioner

The circuit diagram is shown in Fig. 73.

The command pressure produces a force through the K command bellows, and this force produces a torque on the balance beam of the force balance. This torque is opposed by the torque of a measuring spring firmly connected with the balance beam and held tight

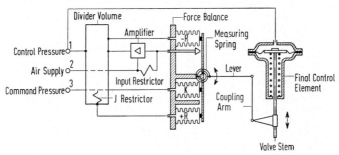

Fig. 73   Single-Acting Positioner Schematic.

by a coupling arm and lever due to the motion of the valve stem. If the two torques differ, the amplifier is actuated through the nozzle as a result of the movement of the balance beam. The output pressure of the amplifier actuates the positioning motor and changes the position until an equilibrium in forces is established on the balance beam of the force balance.

In addition, the amplifier output pressure affects an elastic feedback consisting of two more bellows and a fixed reset action restrictor. With this feedback, the desired transient behavior of the position control is obtained, which improves the dynamic behavior of control loops with positioners.

b) The Pneumatic Power Positioner

The only difference between the power positioner and the single-acting positioner is that the latter has a second pneumatic amplifier built in. Both amplifiers are connected in parallel; i.e., their inputs and outputs are connected together. Thus, the effective output air flow and, consequently, the positioning speed are doubled.

c) The Double-Acting Positioner

The operation is as shown in Fig. 74.
Just as in the single-acting positioner, the torque produced on the force balance by the command bellows is compared with the torque of a measuring spring, the tension of which is proportional to the

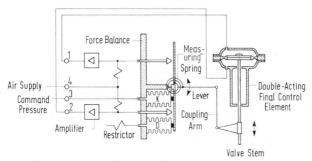

Fig. 74   Double-Acting Positioner Schematic.

position. Mounted on the balance beam are two opposed nozzles, each equipped with a restriction. With a deflection of the balance beam, the air stream is increased by one of the nozzles and throttled by the other one. Thus, behind the nozzles, there are produced two opposed pressures, corresponding to the deflection of the balance beam. Either pressure actuates one of the two pneumatic amplifiers, whose outlets are connected with the two actuating pressure chambers of the double-acting actuator. With a change in command pressure, one amplifier connects one actuating pressure chamber of the motor to the air pressure supply, and the other amplifier connects the second pressure chamber to the atmosphere. As a result, the valve stem is quickly moved and tightens the measuring spring on the force balance until the new equilibrium condition is reached. The result is a permanent difference of pressures in the two actuating pressure chambers. This difference corresponds to the exterior forces on the positioning motor (Fig. 75). To improve the dynamic performance of the positioner, a bellows with a restrictor is mounted on the force balance.

3. Construction

All positioners of the TELEPNEU line are uniformly constructed. The necessary components are plugged into the base plate in the usual way, sealed with "O" rings, and tightened with screws. The input restrictor for the nozzle on the balance beam is screwed into the narrow side of the base plate and can be easily exchanged (Fig. 76).

The restrictor for reset action in a single-acting or a power positioner is inside the base plate and can be replaced after removing the bottom plate (Fig. 76). The bottom plate itself is screwed on the base plate after a gasket has been inserted.

Screwed to the base plate is the connecting plate by which the positioner is fastened to the positioning motor (Fig. 77).

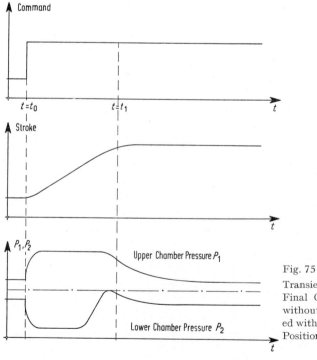

Fig. 75

Transient Behavior of the Final Control Element without Springs combined with a Double-Acting Positioner.

1 Hole for Input Restrictor
2 Base Plate
3 Hole for I Restrictor
4 I Restrictor
5 Input Restrictor

Fig. 76

Single-Acting Positioner,
Bottom Plate Removed.

1 Pressure Gauge
2 Force Balance
3 Amplifier
4 Connecting Plate
5 Measuring Spring
6 Indicating Dial
7 Connection Piece
8 Distributor Panel
  with Switch
9 Lever Shaft Collar

Fig. 77   Single-Acting Positioner, Cover Removed.

On the connecting plate is the mechanism for transmitting the valve travel to the measuring spring on the force balance. The longitudinal motion is converted into a rotating motion by the linkage shown in Fig. 78.

The measurements of the tie rod are adapted to the stroke of the respective motor. On the rotating lever of the linkage are slotted holes marked with the numbers 20, 35, and 75 (Fig. 78). The hinge

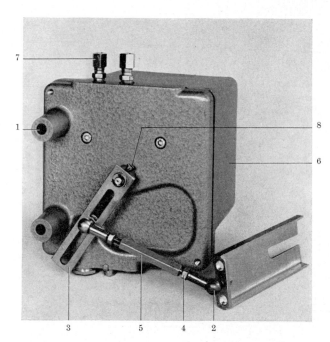

1 Mounting Holes
2 Ball Joint
3 Lever
4 Jam Nut
5 Tie Rod
6 Cover
7 Pressure Connections
8 Retaining Screw

Fig. 78
Positioner, Rear View.

of the tie rod is fixed to the numbered spot corresponding to the stroke of the positioning motor used. If, for reasons of adjustment, the length of the tie rod has to be changed after mounting, this can be done by turning the bolts which have right-hand and left-hand threads and are screwed in at the ends.

Attached to the connecting plates are the Ermeto compression fittings for the outside air connections. In the double-acting and the power positioner, the compression fittings are screwed directly into the connecting plate.

There are, however, different types of single-acting positioners. In the basic Type "a", the compression fittings for actuating air pressure, supply air pressure, and command pressure are also directly screwed into the connecting plate. The Type "b" positioner is equipped with two round pressure gauges for indicating command pressure and actuating pressure. These gauges mount in a distribution panel which is screwed to the connecting plate. The compression fittings for the outside air connections are in this case also attached to the distribution panel. In the Type "c" positioner, an additional switch is furnished in the distribution panel, by which the positioner can be switched off, and by which the command pressure can be fed directly to the positioning motor. A further Type "d" also contains the distribution panel with switch, but no gauges.

4. Testing the Instruments

As with all Telepneu instruments, the positioner components have been separately tested and adjusted. The adjustment and functional testing of the positioners can only be done after the mounting, because the positioners function only after mounting on the positioning motors.

5. Mounting

For mounting, the positioner and the diaphragm motor are screwed together, and the hinge is screwed tightly to that position of the lever corresponding to the stroke of the positioning motor (Fig. 78). Then, the connection piece of the rods is loosely connected to the valve stem. The connections for the air pressure lines are marked with numbers, the meaning of which is seen in the circuit diagrams for the single-acting and double-acting positioners (Figs. 73 and 74). In the power positioner, connections 1 and 2 are the amplifier outputs that go to the diaphragm motor. The command pressure goes to connection 3 and the air pressure to connection 4.

6. Adjustment

Before a diaphragm motor with a positioner is put into operation, the stroke of the motor is made to correspond to the command pressure. This is done by adjusting the zero position and the length of stroke. For this purpose, the command pressure is adjusted to a value corresponding to half of the stroke. The tie rod (Figs. 77 and 78) is screwed to the hinge and its position adjusted until the valve stem has reached mid-position. It is important that the tie rod position be parallel to that of the valve stem. The stroke is now adjusted by shifting the position of the hinge on the lever until the travel range corresponds exactly with the command pressure range. Then, the zero position adjustment must be checked. When the adjustment is finished, the lock nuts on the hinge and on the tie rod strainer are tightened.

The adjustment instructions are basically the same for all positioners. Only when reversing the action of the double-acting positioner (Fig. 79), it is necessary to not only twist the positioner lever but, also, to interchange the actuating pressure lines leading to the diaphragm motor.

a) Adjustment of a Direct Acting Motor

If the motor is direct acting, i.e., the valve stem moves downward with an increase in actuating pressure, then the positioner can be used as furnished because the positioner lever has been pre-adjusted for this type of operation. That means that in the mid-position of the lever, the measuring spring is tensed to one-half of its range. This pre-adjustment is done with the help of the red indicating dial (Fig. 77).

b) Adjustment of a Reverse Acting Motor

Zero position and length of stroke are adjusted in the same way as for the direct acting motor. Here, however, the positioner lever has to be pre-adjusted for this case. After loosening the retaining screw, the lever can be turned by 180°. Its new mid-position is determined when the second notch of the red indicating dial covers the hole in the connecting plate. This mid-position is fixed with a pin, and then the initial tension of the measuring spring is adjusted to one-half of its range. The simplest way to do this is as follows:

The command pressure is adjusted to a value corresponding to the mid-position of the valve stem; normally $0.6\ kg/cm^2$. Then, a pin is put in the hole of the lever shaft collar (Fig. 77) and the measuring spring tightened by twisting until the valve stem moves to the mid-position. In this position, the retaining screw on the lever is securely tightened and the pin is removed from the hole.

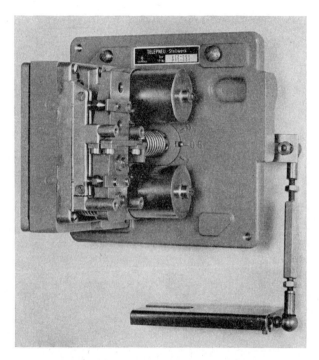

Fig. 79   Double-Acting Positioner, Cover Removed.

c) Adjustment When the Command Pressure Range Has Been Changed

In many cases it is necessary that the positioner command pressure deviates from the normal 0.2 to 1.0 kg/cm² range.

Different pressure ranges, mostly smaller ones, are required if two valves are to operate one after the other.

The input pressure range can be varied by changing the transmission of the valve stem motion to the positioner lever. For this purpose, the pivot point of the hinge on the lever is shifted until a given command pressure range produces the desired stroke. Otherwise, the adjustment is the same as that for a positioner with normal command pressure range.

7. Possibilities of Error

The positioners do not need maintenance when in operation. As an exception, if disturbances occur after long periods of operation, the transmitting rods must be checked and adjusted as necessary. Other disturbances can be practically caused only by plugging of the restrictors when the air supply has not been sufficiently clean. This can be easily eliminated by replacing the components in question.

8. Technical Data

Weight	2 to 3 kg according to type
Normal supply pressure	1.4 kg/cm²
Maximum supply pressure . . .	2.0 kg/cm²
Normal command pressure range	0.2 to 1.0 kg/cm²
Continuously adjustable stroke range	from 20 to 75 mm
Linearity error	<0.5%
Hysteresis	<0.5%
Actuating range	0.3%
Sensitivity	<0.01%
Supply pressure error	0.2% position deviation / 0.1 kg/cm² supply pressure variation

Air consumption:

Single-acting positioner	5 Std. l/min
Double-acting positioner	10 Std. l/min
Power positioner	6 Std. l/min

Maximum output air flow:

Single-acting positioner.	≧ 50 Std. l/min
Double-acting positioner	≧ 50 Std. l/min
Power positioner.	≧ 100 Std. l/min

D. Pneumatic Position Transmitter

1. FUNCTION AND CHARACTERISTICS

The function of a position transmitter is the opposite to that of a positioner; namely, to transform the position of a control valve stem into an air pressure which is proportional to the position. Like the positioner, the position transmitter is attached directly to the positioning motor.

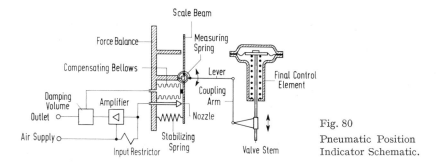

Fig. 80

Pneumatic Position
Indicator Schematic.

A pneumatic amplifier is installed in the instrument. Thus, no indicating lags can arise even if there is a long distance between the position transmitter and the indicating pressure gauge.

The actuating range of the instrument is so negligible that variations in supply pressure or temperature cannot affect the output pressure. The position transmitter is very similar to the positioner in construction and operation. See these sections for a description.

2. PRINCIPLE AND OPERATION

The operation of the position transmitter is shown in Fig. 80. The mechanical coupling elements for transmission of valve stem motion to the force balance are the same as for the positioner. There are the coupling arm, lever, and measuring spring. The torque introduced on the force balance is proportional to the position of the valve stem. This torque is opposed by the torque of a compensating bellows actuated by the output pressure. If the two torques differ, the amplifier is actuated by the nozzle. The amplifier output pressure affects the compensating bellows and varies the position of the balance beam until the output pressure corresponds to the measuring spring tension and, thus, to the valve stem position.

3. CONSTRUCTION

The external construction of the position transmitter differs from the single-acting positioner only in that a single-bellows force balance is used here. According to its special purpose, pressure gauges and switch are not required. Because no special transient behavior quality is required in the position transmitter, an elastic feedback (feedback bellows and fixed reset action restrictor) is not necessary either, so that the indication always follows witn the greatest possible speed.

4. MOUNTING

Like the positioner, the position transmitter is screwed on the diaphragm motor. Valve stem and measuring spring are connected in the same way through the rods. The air pressure supply goes to connection 1 and the indicator to connection 2.

5. ADJUSTMENT

Because the instrument has been constructed from tested and adjusted components, a rough adjustment of the effective length of the measuring spring and the mid-point of the transmission lever is sufficient. The final adjustment of the zero position and range is then done in connection with the positioner.

The measuring spring and the transmission lever are always preadjusted for direct acting diaphragm motors. If the position transmitter is attached to reverse acting motors, the transmission lever is turned by 180⁰, as with the positioner, and the new mid-position is adjusted in the same way by using the red indicating dial (Fig. 81). The adjustment goes like this: The tie rod (Fig. 81) is screwed in the hinge and its position varied until in mid-position of the valve stem the position transmitter output pressure equals 0.6 kg/cm². The connection piece of the rod is twisted vertically to the valve stem until the tie rod is parallel to the valve stem. Then the connecting

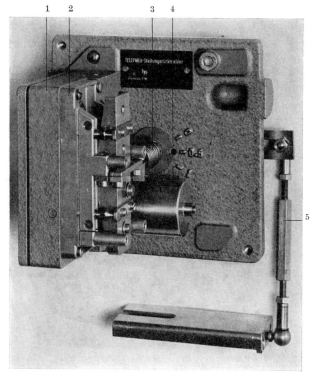

1 Base Plate
2 Force Balance
3 Measuring Spring
4 Amplifier
5 Tie Rod

Fig. 81   Pneumatic Position Transmitter, Cover Removed.

piece is screwed on the valve stem with nut and lock nut. During
this operation the output pressure must not vary. If necessary, the
tie rod has to be readjusted. When shifting the hinge on the transmission lever, care must be taken that the output pressure range of
0.2 to 1.0 kg/cm² should correspond with the positioning range. The
adjustment is possible for strokes from 20 to 75 mm.

6. RELIABILITY IN OPERATION

A position indication independent of the control is in many cases a
valuable aid for plant supervision in addition to measuring and
controlling instruments. Therefore, a high degree of safety and
dependability is required. The rugged components of the TELEPNEU
line furnish this safety to such a degree that no operational maintenance is necessary.

7. TECHNICAL DATA

Dimensions . . . . 177 mm × 150 mm × 162 mm

Normal supply pressure . . . 1.4 kg/cm²

Maximum supply pressure . . 2.0 kg/cm²

Normal output pressure range . 0.2 to 1.0 kg/cm²

Continuously adjustable stroke
    range . . . . from 20 to 75 mm

Linearity error . . . . . . <0.5%

Hysteresis . . . . <0.5%

Actuating range 0.3%

Supply pressure error . $\dfrac{0.2\% \text{ output pressure variation}}{0.1 \text{ kg/cm}^2 \text{ supply pressure variation}}$

Air consumption . . . . . . 5 Std. l/min

E. Pneumatic Control Stations

1. SUMMARY

Control stations are used for the guidance of processes by set point adjustment with automatic control or by pneumatic valve positioning with manual control.

The control stations are plugged into the controllers as tested and adjusted units. Then, together with the recorder, they constitute a complete control entity. Besides, the control stations can be mounted in the panel boards as independent instruments and then can be used for any actuating or switching operation.

The control stations accomplish one of the TELEPNEU system principles: the possibility of bumpless transfer from manual control of a process to automatic control and vice versa without an interlocking or balance position.

The possibility of bumpless transfer exists even if the controller is not in the control room, but mounted on the valve. In this case, when there is a switch-over, the control station supplies a pneumatic signal which switches over the short circuit relay in the controller. The different types of control stations are classified into two groups according to their application and appearance:

In the first group, the front panels of the standard control stations measure 144 mm × 44 mm. This type is designed mainly for control with manually adjusted fixed set point and for simple actuating and switching operations.

In the second group, the front panels of the expanded control stations measure 144 mm × 72 mm. They allow reliable control of complicated control and actuating systems as, for example, controls

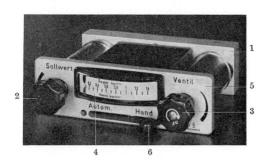

1 Socket
2 Set Point Transmitter
3 Valve Pressure Transmitter
4 Double Pressure Gauge
5 Front Panel
6 Manual-Automatic Switch

Fig. 82
Standard Control Station.

with disturbance feedforward, or ratio and cascade controls with bumpless transfer to fixed set point control of the slave variable.

2. STANDARD CONTROL STATIONS

a) Types and Functions

The standard control stations are produced in six different types.

The basic type (Fig. 82) is mainly designed for simple control loops where the set point is adjusted by hand. The control station contains one precision pressure element each for the set point and the manual valve positioning, a double pressure gauge, and a switch for transferring from automatic to manual operation (AUTOMATIC-MANUAL switch). The double pressure gauge indicates the controller output pressure and the manually adjusted pressure for valve positioning. To allow a bumpless transfer, before the switch is operated, both pressures are assimilated by one of the two pressure elements.

Further fields of application of the control station shown in Fig. 82 are ratio and cascade controls. The front panel of the con-

trol station has been labelled according to the actual application.
Fig. 83 illustrates different types of the standard control station.

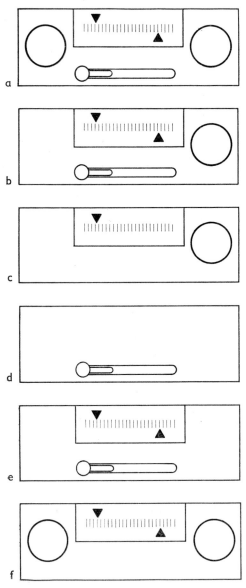

Compared to the standard type (Fig. 83a), Type "b" has no left-hand precision pressure element. This control station is designed mainly for control where the set point is not adjusted by hand. These are controls with a pneumatic time-program transmitter (time-program controls), cascade controls without a manually adjustable effect of the master controller on the slave controller and, finally, electropneumatic controls with electrical set point adjustment.

Type "c" control station has only one precision pressure element and a single pressure gauge and is used as a remote pneumatic control station. The pressure gauge indicates the pressure adjusted on the precision pressure element. Instead of this pressure gauge with only one measuring element, the double pressure gauge used in the Types "a" and "b" can also be installed.

In this way it becomes possible to provide an ad-

Fig. 83   Standard Control Station Models.

ditional indication in the control station; e. g., a valve position indication.

Type "d" contains only a switch which is generally used as a so-called bypass switch.

Type "e" is also used for switching problems but differs from Type "d" in that it is furnished not only with a switch but, also, with a double pressure gauge. The switch is the same as in Type "a"

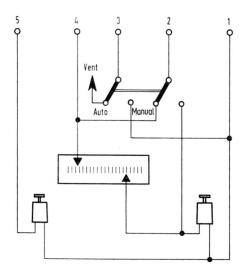

Fig. 84   Standard Control Station.

and, according to its position, allows the optional transmission of one of the two pressures indicated on the double pressure gauge.

Type "f" is designed for pure actuating problems. It contains two precision pressure elements and the double pressure gauge that indicates the adjusted pressures.

b) Circuitry and Operation

The circuit of the standard type control station is shown in Fig. 84. The supply air pressure comes in at connection 1 and goes to both pressure elements and to one pole of the switch. The set point pressure adjusted by the left-hand precision pressure element goes directly to connection 5. The manual actuating pressure is adjusted by the right-hand precision pressure element, goes to the switch, and is indicated by the bottom pointer of the double pressure gauge. The amplifier output pressure of the controller comes in at connection 4 of the switch and is indicated by the top pointer of the double pressure gauge. The line from connection 2 goes to the control valve and the line from connection 3 goes to the short circuit relay if the controller is mounted on the valve. This connection is closed if the control station is used with a board mounted controller having proportional-plus-reset-action or proportional-plus-reset-plus-rate action.

In this last case, the amplifier output pressure goes directly to the diaphragm motor through the AUTOMATIC position of the switch. Before the transfer to MANUAL, the valve pressure element is adjusted until both pointers on the double pressure gauge indicate the same pressure. Then the bumpless AUTO-MANUAL transfer can be made. In the MANUAL position, the pressure in the valve pressure element is switched to the positioning motor. Before switching back from manual to automatic operation, the set point is adjusted until both pointers of the double pressure gauge again indicate the same value. In this case, on the basis of the high controller amplification, the transfer is already bumpless when the top pointer moves between 0.2 and 1.0 kg/cm². If the controller is locally mounted, as mentioned before, the transfer occurs in the short circuit relay of the controller. With the control station in the control room, only the gating signals are given to the short circuit relay at the time of a switchover. In this way, the control loop need not be closed through the control station. The gating signals for the short circuit relay are generated by connecting its control bellows first with the supply pressure and then with the atmosphere.

In Type "b", the set point adjuster and connection 5 are omitted. The operation is the same as in Type "a". Before the transfer from manual to automatic control can occur, the set point pressure supplied to the controller must be varied until the pointers of the double pressure gauge read the same value.

The circuit of a simple remote control station (Type "c") is shown in Fig. 85. The supply air pressure is connected to connection 1 and goes to the precision pressure element. The adjusted pressure is indicated by the pressure gauge and goes to connection 2. When

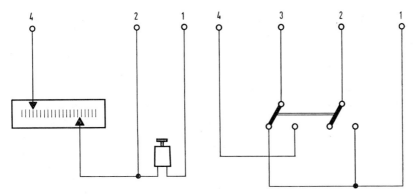

Fig. 85 Type "c" Control Station   Fig. 86 Type "d" Control Station Circuit.
Circuit.

there is a double pressure gauge, the pressure to connection 4 is indicated by the top pointer.

The Type "d" circuit is shown in Fig. 86. With the switch position as shown (BYPASS), connection 1 is tied directly with connection 3.

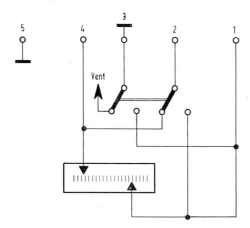

Fig. 87

Type "e" Control Station Circuit.

In the other position, connection 1 is tied with 2 and connection 4 with 3.

In Type "e" the bottom measuring element of the double pressure gauge indicates the pressure in the line from connection 1 (Fig. 87). The pressure in the line from connection 4 is indicated by the pointer of the top measuring element. In the switch position as shown, connection 2 is tied into connection 4; in the other position it is tied into connection 1. The two precision pressure elements are replaced by adapters. Thus, connection 5 is internally blocked in the control station. Connection 3 is blocked from the outside.

The circuit of the double remote control station (Type "f") is shown in Fig. 88. Both precision pressure elements are connected with the

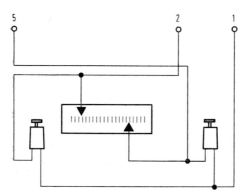

Fig. 88
Type "f" Control Station Circuit.

supply air pressure through connection 1. The pressure set by the left-hand precision pressure element goes to connection 2 and is measured by the top measuring element of the double pressure gauge. The pressure set by the right-hand precision pressure element goes to connection 5 and is indicated by the bottom pointer.

c) Construction

The Figs. 89 to 91 show the construction of the standard-type control station. The base is made of a light metal. Its holes provide the pneumatic communications between the different components. The precision pressure elements and the double pressure gauge are tested separately and are plugged into the base. The seals are "O" ring washers.

The threaded sleeves with their respective precision pressure elements are pressed into the base. The front face is covered by a plastic screen labelled according to the type of control station.

The switch has been designed as a rotary disc valve, whose sliding

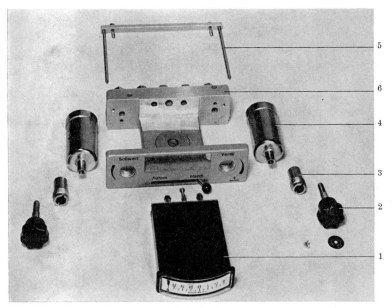

1 Double Pressure Gauge   3 Threaded Sleeve   5 Hold-Down Bolts with Mounting Frame
2 Adjusting Knob   4 Precision Pressure Transmitter   6 Base

Fig. 89   Standard Control Station, Disassembled.

surfaces are lapped and, therefore, are completely tight even in severe service.

The external connections are furnished either as 1/8″ Ermeto compression fittings (Fig. 91) or as plastic plug-in connectors.

d) Mounting

The standard-type control station is often plugged together with the recorder and the plug-in controller to make up an entity. The coupling between controller and control station is accomplished by connecting tubes. They are plugged into the controller connecting panel and are sealed by "O" ring washers (Fig. 91).

Plugging the components together into an entity considerably facilitates their installation. The instruments can be mounted separately as well if this is necessary from the standpoint of control or operation. In this case, the lines are connected to the compression fittings in the usual way.

1 Compression Fittings (Ermeto)
2 Switch

Fig. 90
Standard Control Station, Bottom
View.

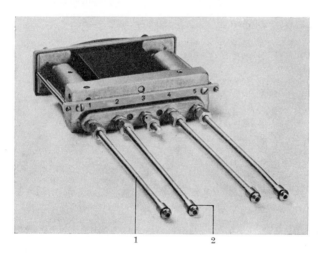

1 Connecting Tubes
2 "O" Ring

Fig. 91
Standard Control
Station,
Rear View.

If, in ratio or cascade controls, a multiplying relay is installed between the control station and the controller connecting plate,
plastic connector plugs are used instead of pipe fittings.
The control station is fastened in the control panel by two hold-
down screws (Fig. 89). The line connections are numbered and their
functions are as seen in the circuit diagrams shown in Figs. 84 to 88.

e) Testing

The testing of the control stations includes checking the individual
components, the tightness of all connector plugs and of the switch.

Testing the standard type:

1. The construction of a convenient test circuit can easily be derived from Fig. 84: A supply air pressure of 1.4 kg/cm² goes through a flowmeter to connection 1. Connection 3 is tightly closed and ports 2 and 4 are connected.

2. A pressure gauge is connected to port 5. By adjusting the set point pressure element every pressure between 0 and 1.2 kg/cm² must be adjustable on the pressure gauge.

3. The suggested test circuit allows simultaneous checking of the valve pressure element and the parallel operation of the elements in the double pressure gauge. By adjusting the valve pressure element, any pressure between 0 and 1.2 kg/cm² must be obtainable. The deviation of the two elements in the range from 0.2 to 1.0 kg/cm² must not exceed 0.028 kg/cm². The air consumption indicated by the flowmeter must not exceed 3 Std. l/min.

Testing Type "b"

The testing is the same as for the standard type, except that there is no set point element.

Testing Type "c"

As for the standard type, the testing is the same here for the functioning of pressure element and pressure gauge (Section 3).

Testing Type "d"

Here only the leakage in the switch has to be tested. Connections 1, 2, 3, and 4 are all connected together and go to the supply air pressure through a flowmeter. The leakage must not exceed 0.2 Std.l/min.

Testing Type "e"

Both measuring elements of the double pressure gauge are tested for their functioning. The tightness of the switch is tested, too. The supply air pressure goes through the flowmeter to connections 1 and 4. Connection 2 is closed.

Testing Type "f"

By turning the precision pressure elements, the pressures in both pressure gauges must be adjustable over the entire range.

f) Interchangeability of the Precision Pressure Elements

The precision pressure elements can be individually interchanged during operation (Fig. 89). If the set point pressure element is to be changed, care must be taken that the switch is in the MANUAL position. Operational maintenance of the control stations is not necessary.

Fig. 92
Expanded Control Station for Ratio Control.

TECHNICAL DATA

Weight	1.4 kg
Supply pressure	1.4 kg/cm²
Air consumption	3 Std. l/min maximum

3. EXPANDED CONTROL STATIONS

a) Types and Functions

The expanded control stations are produced in four different types. The type for ratio and cascade control with a pneumatic multiplying relay allows bumpless transfer to fixed set point control of the slave variable (Fig. 92).

The two precision pressure elements, the double pressure gauge and the switch on the right side of the instrument have the same function as the standard control station and permit bumpless transfer to manual operation of the diaphragm motor of the slave variable. In ratio control, the ratio of controlled to uncontrolled variable is adjusted on the left-hand precision pressure element; in cascade controls, however, the effect of the master controller on the slave controller is adjusted. The ratio or the effect is indicated by an instrument mounted over the recorder (Fig. 93).

The double pressure gauge and the switch on the left allow bumpless transfer from ratio or cascade control to fixed set point control of the slave variable, or vice versa. The set point of the controller

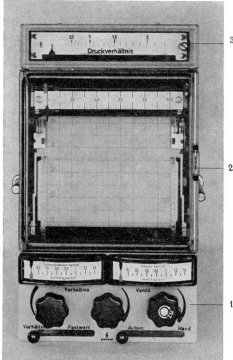

1 Expanded Control Station
2 Recorder
3 Flat Pressure Gauge

3

2

1 Fig. 93

Expanded Control Station for Ratio Control with Pneumatic Recorder and Flat Pressure Gauge for Ratio Indication.

is adjusted by the center precision pressure element. It is indicated by the lower pointer of the left-hand pressure gauge. The output pressure of the multiplying relay is indicated on the upper scale.

Type "b" (Fig. 94) differs from Type "a" in that it has no left-hand precision pressure element. It is used only in connection with the multiplying relay and is designed for cascade-ratio controls. Here, the ratio is not set to a fixed value by hand as in Type "a", but is

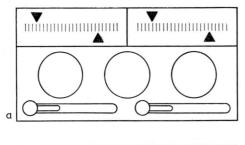

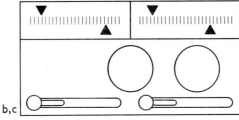

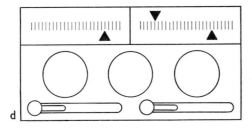

Fig. 94   Expanded Control Station Models.

adjusted by a master in-strument; e.g., a controller or a transmitter. Other-wise, the function is exact-ly the same as Type "a".
Control station Type "c" is exactly like Type "b", as far as circuit, instrument layout and front view are concerned. However, it is always used without a multiplying relay and is forseen for simple cascade controls with the possibili-ty of bumpless transfer to fixed set point control. The output pressure of the master controller is indi-cated by the upper pointer of the left-hand double pressure gauge. Adjust-ment with and transfer to fixed set point control of the slave variable are ac-complished in the same way as in Types "a" and "b". Differing from Type "b", it has Ermeto compression fittings screwed in the back of the instrument.
Type "d" has the same applications as Type "a". However, bump-less transfer to fixed set point control has been eliminated. The left-hand pressure gauge is a single instrument and indicates the adjusted ratio. A pressure gauge above the recorder as in Fig. 93 is then no longer required.

b) Circuitry and Operation

The operation of control station Type "a" can be seen in Fig. 95. The supply air pressure is connected to port 1. From there, the air pressure goes to three precision pressure elements and to one pole of the MANUAL-AUTOMATIC switch.

The pressure which creates the ratio or the command influence in the multiplying relay is adjusted on the left-hand precision pressure element. It goes directly to connection 7. The set point pressure for fixed set point control of the slave variable is adjusted by the center precision pressure element and is indicated by the lower pointer of the left-hand double pressure gauge. When the switch is in FIXED SET POINT CONTROL position, this pressure goes to port 5. The output pressure of the multiplying relay is at connection 8 and is indicated by the upper pointer of the left-hand double pressure gauge. This pressure goes to the other pole of the routing switch. In the RATIO or CASCADE position of the switch it also goes to connection 5. The transfer from ratio or cascade control to fixed set point control is done bumplessly if both pointers of the left-hand pressure gauge indicate equal pressures. This is accomplished by adjustment of center set point transmitter. Before switching back to ratio or cascade control, the pressures on the left-hand pressure gauge are equilibrated by the left-hand precision pressure element.

The transfer to manual actuation of the control valve is the same as for the standard control station. The function can be easily seen from Fig. 95. It may be mentioned that this bumpless transfer is possible in both operating conditions.

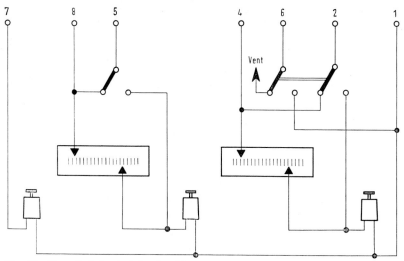

Fig. 95 Type "a" Control Station Circuit.

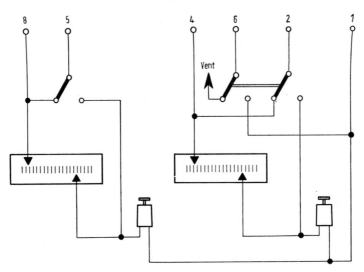

Fig. 96   Types "b" and "c" Control Station Circuits.

Fig. 96 shows the circuit for Type "b". As mentioned before, this control station is used for cascade ratio control. It is always used in conjunction with the multiplying relay. Comparison with the schematic for Type "a" (Fig. 94) shows that only the left-hand precision pressure element and connection 7 are omitted. Therefore, the pressure indicated by the top pointer of the left-hand double pressure gauge can no longer be varied from the control station.

The transfer from fixed set point control to cascade ratio control and vice versa is bumpless when both pressures indicated by the left-hand pressure gauge have been equalized. This is done by adjusting the center precision pressure element.

For transferring from manual control of the slave variable to cascade ratio control, the equalizing of both pressures in the right-hand pressure gauge can only be done through adjusting the right-hand pressure transmitter, unless the control station of the master controller is used.

All other switching operations are as for Type "a".

The operation of Type "c" can also be seen from Fig. 96. The control station is used for simple cascade controls without a multiplying relay. The master instrument (transmitter, controller, or control station) is connected at port 8. The top pointer of the left-hand double pressure gauge indicates this pressure. All transferring and equalizing operations are the same as for Type "b".

Type "d" control station (Fig. 97) is used for ratio control with multiplying relay. The left-hand pressure gauge indicates the pressure adjusted by the left-hand pressure transmitter, this pressure being a measure of the ratio adjusted in the multiplying relay. The switching possibilities are the same as in Type "a", except that the left-hand switch can no longer be operated bump-free.

c) Construction

The construction of expanded control stations can be seen from Figs. 98 and 99, using the standard Type "a" as an example.

As in the simple control station, the socket is made of light metal and the air connections to individual components are bored holes. Similar to the simple control station, the components are fastened to the base in the same way. The rotary disc valves are lever operated (Fig. 98) to achieve the required switching angle even with the reduced switch travel.

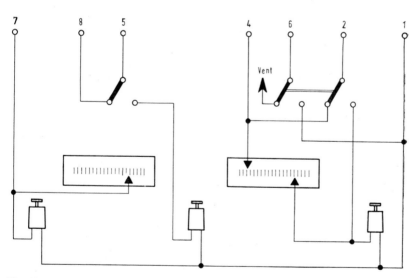

Fig. 97   Type "d" Control Station Circuit.

In Types "a", "b", and "d", the air passages terminate in smooth bores. Control station and multiplying relay are screwed together. Type "c" is always used without a multiplying relay. Therefore, the external air connections are furnished as Ermeto compression fittings having 1/8" connections on one end and 6 mm tubing on the other.

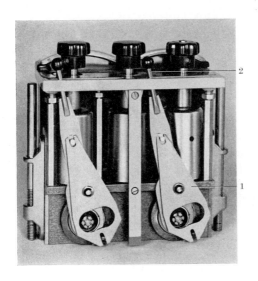

1 Rotary Disc Valve
2 Switch Lever

Fig. 98   Type "a" Expanded Control Station, Bottom View.

d) Mounting

The expanded control stations are also generally tied into the other control board instruments by plug-in connections, no matter whether they are coupled with a multiplying relay or not. Fastening to the panel board is with mounting brackets and studs (Fig. 99).

4. Testing

As for the simple control stations, component functioning and tightness of connections and switches are all tested.

    Testing Type "a"

1. An appropriate test circuit can be set up according to Fig. 95. For this purpose, ports 2 and 4 are connected as are 5 and 8. Connection 6 is closed. The switch positions required for the testing

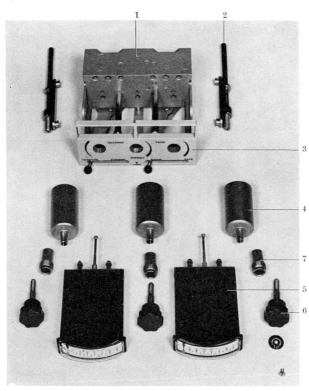

1 Base
2 Mounting Brackets and Studs
3 Front Panel
4 Precision Pressure Transmitter
5 Double Pressure Gauge
6 Adjusting Knob
7 Threaded Sleeve

Fig. 99   Components of the Expanded Control Stations.

are MANUAL and FIXED SET POINT CONTROL. The supply air goes through a flowmeter to connection 1, and a supply air pressure of 1.4 kg/cm² is set.

2. Any pressure between 0 and 1.2 kg/cm² adjusted with the left-hand pressure transmitter must be obtainable on a pressure gauge connected with port 7.

3. By adjusting the center pressure transmitter, both measuring elements of the left-hand double pressure gauge must be adjustable between 0 and 1.2 kg/cm². In the range 0.2 to 1.0 kg/cm², the two indications must not differ by more than 0.028 kg/cm². In the same way, the right-hand pressure element is tested with its respective double pressure gauge. The air consumption indicated by the flow-meter must not exceed 4.5 Std.l/min.

Testing Control Station Types "b" and "c"

Except for section 2 the testing is the same as for Type "a".

Testing Control Station Type "d"

1. A test circuit is set up according to Fig. 97 as follows:

Put the right-hand switch into MANUAL position and the left-hand switch into FIXED SET POINT CONTROL position. Connect port 2 with port 4. Close connections 6 and 7 and connect a pressure gauge to connection 5. Bring supply air through a flowmeter to connection 1 and adjust supply air pressure to 1.4 kg/cm^2.

2. The testing of the right-hand pressure element and the double pressure gauge is done as for Type "a" (see section 3). The functioning of the two remaining pressure transmitters is tested by the left-hand pressure gauge or by an external pressure gauge. The air consumption must not exceed 4.5 Std. l/min.

5. Sources of Error and Repair

The control stations are rugged and not susceptible to disturbances. If, in spite of this, disturbances occur during operation, they probably originate from dirt in the capillary restrictions in the precision pressure elements. This can only happen when the supply air is not sufficiently filtered.

Because the expanded control stations contain the same components as the simple units, maintenance is superfluous here as well.

6. Technical Data

Dimensions . . . . 144 mm × 72 mm × 154 mm
Weight . . . . 2.3 kg approx.
Supply pressure . . . . 1.4 kg/cm^2
Air consumption . . . . . . 4.5 Std.l/min maximum

F. Pneumatic Standard Recorders

1. Summary

Pneumatic standardized control systems also include recorders. The latter record the course of the measured values. Correlated values, such as set point and actual value, should be recorded together. These recorders are used in great quantities in the chemical process industries, particularly in the petroleum industry and are, therefore, designed as "miniature instruments" (Fig. 100). Only in this way can panel boards be clearly designed and the supervision made possible of the numerous control instruments that are concentrated in a modern control room.

The pneumatic recorders of the TELEPNEU System, with their front

1 Lever for Recording Unit
2 Pinion
3 Lever for Swivel Table
4 Door Closure
5 Metal Housing

Fig. 100   TELEPNEU Strip Chart Recorder (Front View).

panel dimensions of 144 mm × 144 mm, completely meet these requirements. According to the respective application, one, two, or three measuring elements are installed in the recorders, of which two at the most can be recording.

The measuring elements are always designed for the standard pressure range of 0.2 to 1.0 kg/cm², corresponding to a scale graduation of 0 to 100%. The effective paper width is 100 mm. The recording paper moves vertically from top to bottom. The length of paper visible is 90 mm.

The measured values are indicated or recorded by pen guides in rectangular coordinates.

The recorder is made of rugged, individual components that afford overrange protection up to 300% of full range pressure.

With just a few hand operations, proportional, proportional-plus-

reset action or proportional-plus-reset-plus-rate action plug-in controllers can be mounted on the rear of the recorder. A TELEPNEU
control station can be installed on the controller and, together with
controller and recorder, thus makes a complete control unit (Fig.101).
By throttling the signal pressures with needle valves, the recorder
measuring elements can be optionally damped. The adjusting screws

1 TELEPNEU
  Recorder
2 Plug-In Controller
3 Control Station

Fig. 101   Complete Control Unit with TELEPNEU Recorder, Plug-In Controller
and Control Station.

for zero, the measuring range, and the damping are accessible from
the front of the recorder.
An electric, self-starting synchronous motor is used for the chart
drive. In the standard types, the paper speed is 20 mm/hour. There
are special types available for other chart speeds.

2. THE COMPONENTS

a) Measuring Elements

Bellows-spring measuring elements are used for the single, double
and triple measuring elements. The measuring element housings
are so rugged that mechanical damage to the measuring element is
practically impossible.

The double and triple measuring elements are shown in Fig. 102. The external appearance of the single measuring element is identical with the double measuring element, except that one housing is empty.

The operation of a bellows-spring element is shown in Fig. 103. The signal pressure goes through an adjustable restrictor to the

1 Double Measuring Element

2 Triple Measuring Element

Fig. 102 Double and Triple Measuring Elements for Pneumatic Recorders.

measuring bellows. By means of the restrictor, the damping can be adjusted. The movement of the measuring bellows against the measuring spring is proportional to the supplied signal pressure. This movement is transferred to the angle lever through a connecting rod. Flexibly connected with the angle lever is the swivel arm which lifts itself off of the angle lever when the measuring bellows is overloaded. The swivel arm transfers the motion further to the pen carriage.

If the signal pressure of 1.0 kg/cm², which corresponds to full scale, is exceeded, the bottom of the measuring bellows touches a stop and, thus, protects the other transmitting elements from damage.

Besides the damping of the measuring pressure mentioned before, the signal range and the zero point are adjustable on the measuring element as well. The adjusting screws are easily accessible from the front of the measuring element (Fig. 102). The measuring range is adjusted by changing the number of effective turns of the measuring spring and the zero point by changing the tension in the measuring spring (Fig. 103).

b) Scale Holder with Guide

The recording is done in rectangular coordinates. This facilitates evaluation of the diagrams. In the TELEPNEU recorder a carriage

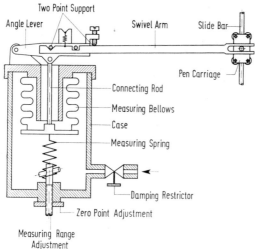

Fig. 103

Measuring Element of a Pneumatic Recorder.

leads the pen over the paper, resulting in a positive guide. The carriage is connected by a pin to the swivel arm of the movable element (Fig. 103). Slide bars, carriage and scale are all assembled into one component called the scale holder (Fig. 104).

With the transmission of the bellows motion to the pen carriage, there is a curvature error which here, however, because of the long swivel arm, is negligible and never exceeds 0.6% of the measuring range.

c) Recording Unit

The recording unit's function is to contain the paper feed roll, to lead the paper over the swivel table and to take it up again. Paper transport is accomplished by a cog wheel which fits the perforations in the paper (Figs. 105 and 106).

The cog wheel and the take-up reel are driven by the same motor. To always keep the paper stretched, the take-up reel is so driven by a slip clutch that it tends to move faster than the required take-up speed. The slip clutch torque required for a satisfactory motion of the paper is adjustable by the tension of a helical spring (Fig. 107). Another slip clutch between

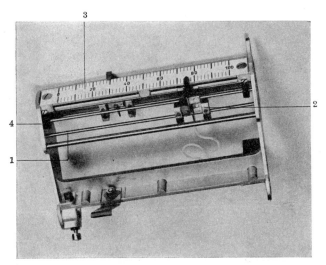

1 Slide Bar
2 Pen Carriage
3 Scale
4 Scale Holder

Fig. 104
Scale Holder.

the cog wheel and reduction gear allows the manual paper transport over a pinion.

A special feature of the TELEPNEU recorder is the automatic break-in and take-up of the paper. Two rubber pieces are fixed to the take-up reel for picking up the moving paper to roll it up.

For removing the paper from the take-up chamber, the swivel table is tilted by moving the spring lever (Fig. 106) to the right and the take-up reel can then be taken out. When putting in the empty take-up reel, care must be taken that it sits snugly in its support and that the inscription FRONT is readable on the rubber pieces. When the swivel table is tilted back, the lever locks again.

d) Drive Motor

The speed of the motor (375 rpm) may be geared down when required by a gear train. For special types, the drive motor is furnished for different operating voltages and frequencies. The motor and gear drive are in a box and need no maintenance.

e) Ink Duct

The ink goes from the storage bottle through a thin tube to the writing pen. Near movable parts, the connection is made with flexible plastic hoses (Fig. 109).

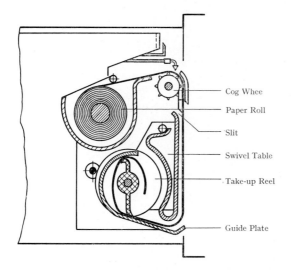

Cog Whee

Paper Roll

Slit

Swivel Table

Take-up Reel

Guide Plate

Fig. 105

Paper Feed in the Recording Unit.

3. Construction and Mounting

The individual components of the pneumatic recorder—measuring elements, recording unit, chart drive motor, and scale holder—are mounted in a rugged housing. The measuring elements are carefully held by pins.

The recording unit can be swung out to allow the chart roll to be inserted after a lever, which also holds the scale, has been raised. Serving as bearings are two guide pins which sit in two slides of the housing and allow removal of the entire recording unit (Figs. 106 and 108). When the recording unit has been removed, all other components are easily accessible from the front. It is then possible to easily replace the ink bottles or to adjust the measuring system parameters.

The electric connection is on the side. The Ermeto compression fittings for the pressure lines are on the rear panel. The lines are arranged from top to bottom in the same order as the pointers and pens.

For installation in the panel board, the electric connection panel

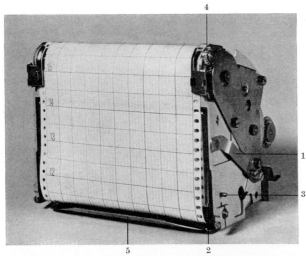

1 Spring Lever
2 Swivel Table
3 Guide Pin
4 Pinion
5 Guide Plate

Fig. 106
Recording Unit.

1 Helical Spring
2 Slip Clutch
3 Reduction Gear

Fig. 107
Recording Unit,
Rear View.

has to be removed. The recorder is then front-mounted into the panel board cutout and fastened by hold-down studs which go through brackets on the side walls of the instrument. After the electric supply cable has been pulled through the conduit fitting on the electric connection panel, it is connected to the terminal board. Then, the connection panel can be put back again (Fig. 109).

4. TYPES

The various recorder types differ in number and arrangement of the measuring elements, in the chart paper speed, and in the operating voltages and frequencies.

a) Standard Types

One pneumatic recording measuring element.
Two pneumatic measuring elements; one recording and one indicating.
Two pneumatic measuring elements; both recording.
Three pneumatic measuring elements; two recording and one indicating.
All standard types are designed for a chart speed of 20 mm/hour and for operation on 220 volt, 50-cycle power.

b) Special Types

Special types are obtained from varying the standard type combinations of measuring elements for different chart speeds, operating voltages, and frequencies.

5. ADJUSTMENT AND TESTING

The separate components are individually preset and tested during manufacturing. Thus, only small adjustments are necessary in assembling the recorder. This is an advantage, especially for installing spare parts in instruments that are already mounted and operating. When checking the recorder, it has first to be ascertained that all the swivel arms and slide bar carriages move freely and unhampered over the whole travel range.
At both ends of the slide bars are stops for the pen carriages. These

1 Lever
2 Slide Guides
3 Set Screws for
  Measuring Element
  Parameters

Fig. 108   Pneumatic Recorder, Recording Unit Removed.

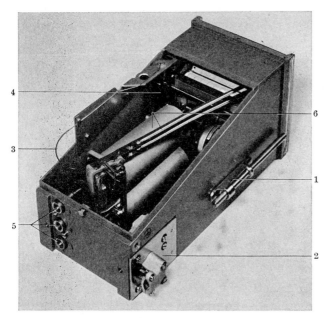

1 Mounting Bracket
  with Stud
2 Electric Connec-
  tion Panel
3 Connections for
  Pressure Lines
4 Ink Bottle
5 Ink Feed
6 Measuring Element
  with Pointer Lever

Fig. 109   Pneumatic Recorder, Sheet Metal Housing Removed.

should be so adjusted that the pen clears the side paper perforations at each extreme of its travel.

The 0% and 100% lines of the paper must match up with the corresponding marks on the scale. This can be accomplished by shifting the scale.

To provide a check of the measuring elements during operation, standard reference pressure gauges can be connected in parallel with the measuring elements. The hose fittings for this are accessible after the recorder unit has been removed. If it is necessary to correct the zero point or measurement range, this is done with the adjusting screws provided for this purpose (Fig. 108). It is necessary to adjust the zero point each time the measurement range has been corrected.

6. Putting into Operation and Maintenance

Before the recorder can be put into operation, the safety stops on the pen carriages, put there for transportation, have to be removed. Then the following work has to be done:

a) Filling the Ink Bottles

After removing the recording unit, the ink bottles can be removed from their fixtures and filled. Then they are replaced so that the holding spring locks.

b) Inserting the Chart Roll

To insert the paper, the recording unit is swung out and the roll placed in the trough. Then the unit is swung back and the paper led over the cog wheel with the hinged guides tilted (Fig. 106). The cogs must so engage the perforations that the paper travels straight. Further work is not necessary because the paper moves and is taken up automatically.

c) Starting the Recording

The capillary action of the ink duct provides a continuous flow of ink, which is a prerequisite for a clean record. However, when starting up the recorder the ink must be first pressured up to the pen. This is done by pressuring the ink bottle with a squeeze bulb.

For this an air pressure line goes from the ink bottle to the front (Fig. 110).

If a recorder has been out of operation for some time, it is possible that the ink in the pen has dried up. The pen can be easily removed from the pen carriage and cleaned.

d) Removing the Chart Paper

In the process industries, daily charts are frequently collected. In this case, the recorder is used without a take-up reel because the

1 Connection for Squeeze Bulb
2 Swivel Table
3 Take-up Reel
4 Knife Edge

Fig. 110   Unrolling Used Chart Paper after Tilting the Swivel Table in the Recording Unit.

unrolled short chart run can be taken up in the collecting trough. For cutting off the daily chart a knife edge is found at the top of the swivel table. If no daily charts are taken, the paper is continuously stored on the take-up reel.

In this case, it is also possible to examine any desired length of chart run. The swivel table is opened and the paper is pulled off the reel. By turning a flange of the take-up reel, the paper is easily rolled up again.

When a take-up reel is full, it is lifted out of its fixture after opening the swivel table. The chart roll can be removed by first removing an end flange of the take-up reel and then slightly twisting it back and forth.

e) Maintenance

Aside from checking the ink duct, especially in non-continuous operation, the recorder needs no maintenance. After two years of service, the plastic hoses of the ink duct must be replaced by the spare ones furnished at the time of purchase.

G. Pneumatic Indicators

1. INDICATION AND CONTROL OF PROCESS AND SYSTEM VARIABLES

To safely and easily control complicated processes, operating variable values—as well as the most important system variables—have to be supervised and controlled. For example, system variables are set points, manual control pressures, controller output pressures, and ratio values or disturbances in cascade controls. These pose two different problems; simple indication of measured values and comparison of two system variables which have to be balanced. If process variables are to be indicated, the instruments must meet the same high precision requirements as do transmitters, recorders, and controllers. On the other hand, for indication of system variables, the measuring precision is in most cases of secondary importance.

2. FUNCTIONS AND TYPES

The monitoring of system variables is an essential problem, especially when transferring from manual to automatic operation or vice versa. Here, controller output pressure and manual control pressure have to be measured and balanced so that a bumpless transfer without intermediate position can take place. For this purpose the TELEPNEU technique uses double pressure gauges in the control stations.

The pointers of the two instruments are adjusted for accuracy in synchronization and move in front of a common scale so that balancing them is an easy matter (Fig. 111). Similar problems arise in ratio and cascade controls where there must be a bumpless transfer from master control to fixed set point operation. These miniature pressure gauges are used only for indicating system variables and it is then possible to use the instrument either as a double or as a single pressure gauge.

Fig. 111   Double Pressure Gauge (72 mm × 24 mm).

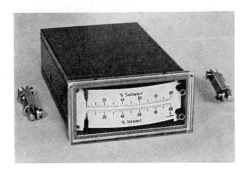

Fig. 112   Double Pressure Gauge (144 mm × 72 mm).

For all problems where a higher absolute indicating precision is required, a board mounted pressure gauge with a scale length of 100 mm is used. These miniature gauges are used as double or as single instruments and have respective front panel dimensions of 144 mm × 72 mm and 144 mm × 36 mm (DIN 47700), as seen in Figs. 112 and 113.

The 144 mm × 72 mm double model is mainly used in TELEPNEU

controllers without recorders for comparing the set point and measured values.

The single pressure gauge (144 mm × 36 mm) is mainly used for indicating the set point value in electropneumatic controllers where the electrically measured instantaneous value is recorded by an electric recorder and where the set point is measured pneumatically and indicated separately. Besides the indication of set point and measured value, both instruments can be used for any measurement problem.

Their dimensions and shapes facilitate a universality in instrumentation within the scope of the TELEPERM-TELEPNEU System.

Fig. 113   Single Pressure Gauge (144 mm × 36 mm).

3. CONSTRUCTION AND MOUNTING

The measuring elements of the pneumatic indicators uniformly have for sensing systems a spirally coiled Bourdon spring of about 2 or 3 turns.

The outer end of the measuring spring is fixed in a spring holder (Figs. 114 and 115) and takes the pressure capillary. The pointer is connected directly to the free end of the measuring spring with no intermediate gear ratio. To adjust the measurement range, the pick-off is shifted to the free end of the spring. The pointer shaft has jewel pivots and is connected to the pointer through the zero point adjustment slip clutch. To suppress pressure shocks a damping device, consisting of a restrictor and a volume, is connected in series to each measuring spring.

a) Double Pressure Gauges (72 mm × 24 mm)

Both sensing systems of the double pressure gauge (72 mm × 24 mm) are mounted on a common base plate (Fig. 115). The damping volumes are pressed into the base plate. After loosening both fastening screws of any system holder, that system can be removed as an entity. The scale is screwed to the base plate with two screws. Both sensing systems are protected against mechanical damages by a protective shell having a Plexiglas window in the front. The double gauge is plugged into the control station and fastened with a screw. The range is standard from 0 to 1.4 kg/cm^2.

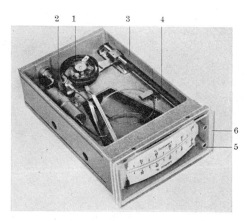

1 Measuring Spring
2 Damping Volume
3 Housing
4 Spindle
5 Zero Setting
6 Plexiglas Window

Fig. 114
Double Pressure Gauge
(144 mm × 72 mm) Assembly.

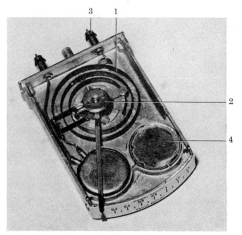

1 Measuring Spring
2 System Holder
3 Plug-In Connections
4 Damping Volume

Fig. 115
Double Pressure Gauge
(72 mm × 24 mm) Assembly.

b) Pressure Gauges (144 mm × 72 mm and 144 mm × 36 mm)

In these pressure gauges, the measuring system holders rotate around the pointer shaft. Thus, the measuring systems can be externally rotated for zero point adjustment by a spindle.The adjustment is done from the front of the instrument with a screwdriver. The gauge housings consist of a light metal casting enclosed by sheet metal covers. The Plexiglas windows in front of the scales are screwed in the housing. In the back of the pressure gauges are the

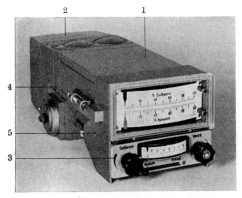

1 Double Pressure Gauge
2 TELEPNEU Plug-In Controller
3 Control Station
4 Controller Connection Panel
5 Mounting Bracket

Fig. 116   Complete Control Unit with Pneumatic Set Point and Actual Value
Indicator, Control Station, and TELEPNEU Plug-In Controller.

Ermeto compression fittings for the air supply lines. Should it be desired to plug in a TELEPNEU controller, additional connections are provided. There are two standard measurement ranges: 0 to 1.0 and 0 to 1.6 kg/cm².

The gauge is fastened to the panel board by means of screws which go through mounting brackets installed in holes located in the side panels of the housing (Fig. 112). When a double pressure gauge is used with a plug-in controller and a control station for indicating set point and actual values, a mounting bracket is used for the common fastening of the pressure gauge and control station (Fig. 116).

The bracket is held against the panel by the tightening screws. Here, a special controller connection panel is used, in which the air connections and the reversing switch are arranged laterally.

4. TECHNICAL DATA

a) *Double Pressure Gauge (72 mm × 24 mm)*

Dimensions:

Front frame . . . . 72 mm × 24 mm
Width of housing . . . . 66 mm
Height of housing . . . . 19.5 mm
Depth without connection fittings . . . 82 mm
Scale length . . . . 52 mm

Weight . . . . 180 grams approx.
Measurement range . . . . 0 to 1.4 kg/cm²
Quality class 2
Synchronization accuracy 2%

b) *Double Pressure Gauge (144 mm × 72 mm)*

Dimensions:

Front frame . . . . 144 mm × 72 mm
Width of housing . . . . 136 mm
Height of housing . . . . 64 mm
Depth without connection fittings . . . 215 mm
Scale length . . . . 100 mm

Weight . . . . 1850 grams
Measuring range - optional . . . . . . 0 to 1.0 kg/cm²
                     or   0 to 1.6 kg/cm²
Quality class 1
Synchronization accuracy 1%

c) *Pressure Gauge (144 mm × 36 mm)*

Dimensions:

Front frame . . . . 144 mm × 36 mm
Width of housing . . . . 136 mm
Height of housing . . . . 32 mm
Depth without connection fittings . . . 220 mm
Scale length . . . . 100 mm

Weight . . . . 1070 grams
Measuring range - optional . . . . . . 0 to 1.0 kg/cm²
                     or   0 to 1.6 kg/cm²
Quality class 1

H. Pneumatic Multiplying Relay

1. FUNCTION

A complete line of instruments for pneumatic control in the process industries must contain a satisfactorily operating instrument for pressure multiplication. For example, it is advantageous in pneumatic ratio control if the desired ratio between two flows, which are transduced into pressures by flow transmitters, can be remotely adjusted by a third pressure. In this connection, the constancy in a once-adjusted ratio for different loads is of greater importance than the linear relation between the ratio and the pressure creating this ratio. For a ratio to be stably adjusted by a pressure, a linear relationship must exist between the two other pressures.

Of special importance is an exceptional lack of sensitivity—and, zero thus, an extreme stability—to disturbances which may result from stopping up of restrictors and nozzles caused by a variation of the auxiliary air pressure, or from a change in ambient temperature, or of instrument air. In addition, a certain degree of mechanical ruggedness must be inherent should the device be used in processing industries.

Another requirement is ease of adjustment and the possibility of installation in the standardized control system. The electropneumatic building block concept of the TELEPERM-TELEPNEU control system ties these requirements in with the question of easy plug-in to controllers and control stations.

By using multiplying relays in ratio controls, the ratio between two process variables—e.g., two flows—results as a stable pressure adjusted either manually or by a variable pressure (master controller, ratio program transmitter).

In cascade controls, the influence of the master controller on the set point of the slave controller can be additionally changed through multiplication using a manually adjusted pressure.

Many different pneumatic and electropneumatic circuit combinations can be built with multiplying relays. Together with expanded control stations of the TELEPERM-TELEPNEU System, multiplying devices can afford comprehensive solutions to even the most complicated control problems. Only to be mentioned here is the possibility of a simply constructed cascade ratio control with bumpless transfer to fixed set point control of different process variables.

2. Principle

a) Pneumatic Multiplication

Pneumatic instruments for the addition and subtraction of pressures can be constructed quite simply and dependably by applying the principle of force balance. Moreover, a high measurement accuracy

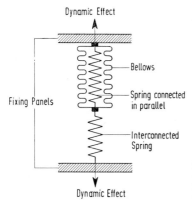

Fig. 117
Forces of a Bellows-Spring System on Two Panels.

can thus be obtained, as shown by the Telepneu force balance where measuring tolerances of 0.2% are achieved without special calibration requirements.

Historically, obtaining measurement accuracy with pressure multiplication presented considerable difficulties. From the outset, the deflection balance devices had to be eliminated because of the hysteresis action of the spring elements and the transfer units which proved to be, in this case, particularly disturbing. Multiplication based on force balance confronted research with completely new problems. A solution using the Telepneu technique is described below.

If bellows are stretched between two fixed panels, then as a result of a pressure bellows effect, forces are exerted on the panels which are proportional to this pressure and to the effective area of the bellows. A spring inserted between the bellows and one of the two panels does not, at first, change the force action of the bellows if the spring constant of the bellows is negligible compared with the effective forces (Fig. 117).

If, however, a stronger spring is connected in parallel to the weak one of the bellows, the forces exerted on the panels become weaker in proportion to the expansion of the bellows and the interconnected spring. The forces exerted by the bellows on the panels are now a function of the product of the bellows pressure and the spring constant of the interconnected spring.

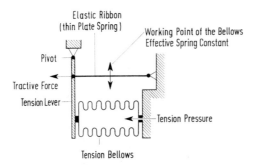

Fig. 118   Spring with Pneumatically Adjustable   Fig. 119   Pneumatic Multi-
            Spring Tension.   plying Relay.

A spring with pneumatically adjustable tension is shown in Fig. 118. Here, one end of a thin metal ribbon is firmly mounted in a frame while the other end is fixed to a tension lever that moves about a pivot. Through this lever the ribbon is affected by a tension that is proportional to the tension pressure of a bellows connected with the lever. The spring tension effective in the middle between the two fixed ends of the ribbon and normal to the direction of the tractive force is proportional to this force and, thereby, proportional to the pressure in the bellows.

If the pneumatic spring is used instead of the interconnected spring shown in Fig. 117 and if, moreover, the bellows are equipped with a circular spring for reasons of guidance and zero stability, the resulting arrangement is as shown in Fig. 119. On the panel at the top end of the circular spring bellows a force is exerted that corresponds to the product of the pressures in both bellows.

b) Compensation of the Product

The panel connected to the upper end of the circular spring bellows is now replaced by the balance beam of a standard pneumatic force balance. In this force balance, a self-acting compensation system consisting of compensating bellows, a nozzle, and a pneumatic amplifier counter-balances the actuating force which corresponds to the product of the two input pressures (Fig. 120). Thus, the outlet pressure of the compensating bellows is controlled and is a measure of the product of inlet pressures 1 and 2.

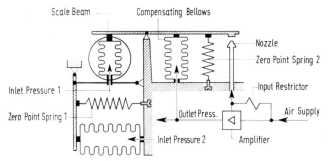

Fig. 120   Self-acting Compensation of the Product of Two Inlet Pressure Variables.

c) Adjusting the Zero Points

To adapt the pressure ranges of the multiplying relay to the measured variable pressures, the controller outlet pressures, and the set point pressure of the standard pneumatic system, each of the three bellows is equipped with a zero point spring, by which the zero point tension is adjusted for each pressure. The zero point springs of the inlet pressure 2 bellows and of the outlet pressure are arranged in parallel with the bellows. Their spring tensions can be changed with set screws. For the inlet pressure 1 bellows the circular spring acts as a zero balance spring. Its initial tension is adjustable by turning the nozzle (Fig. 120).

By varying inlet pressure 2 over the range of 0.2 to 1.0 kg/cm^2, the ratio between the inlet pressure 1 and the outlet pressure is continuously varied from 0.5 to 2. For ratio controls, the zero points of inlet pressure 1 and outlet pressure must be adjusted to

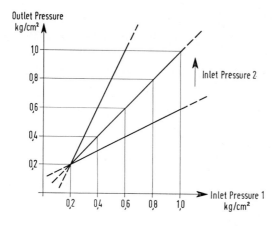

Fig. 121

Multiplying Relay
Characteristic Curves for
Ratio Control.

0.2 kg/cm². The characteristic curves of the instrument then inter-
sect at the 0.2 kg/cm² point (Fig. 121).

For cascade controls, the zero points of inlet pressure 1 and
outlet pressure are adjusted to 0.6 kg/cm² which is the mid-point
of the range (Fig. 122). The intersection of the characteristic curves
can also be optionally adjusted between the input and output pressure ranges. Sometimes this is desirable for specific purposes; for
example, special disturbance feedforwards.

When the ratio pressure is changed, the output pressure stability
is very high at the point of curve intersection. It amounts to

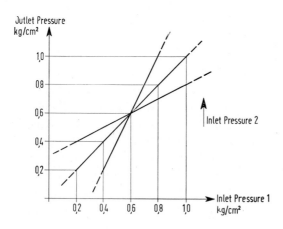

Fig. 122

Multiplying Relay
Characteristic Curves for
Cascade Control.

about 0.2 to 0.3% of the outlet pressure range for a change in inlet pressure 2 over the entire range. This is of particular importance for the quality of ratio controls.

3. CONSTRUCTION

Figures 123 and 124 show how the internal components of the multiplying relay are set up.

The balance beam is mounted without friction by two spring bands. A stop prevents overloading. The nozzle is so dimensioned that it serves as a stop itself. To balance the torque, only the compensating bellows has to be shifted. It can be precisely adjusted by means of an eccentric on the force balance. The elastic ribbon is

Fig. 123
TELEPNEU Multiplying
Relay Insert.

fixed with clamps to the tension device and to the circular spring system. The tension lever is bedded without friction in a bearing with transversely jointed spring bands. The zero point springs of compensating and tension bellows are tension springs. They can be initially stressed with adjusting screws. To initially stress the circular spring system, the nozzle can be adjusted and for this purpose it is guided in an "O" ring packing. To avoid hysteresis, the force of the bellows installed in the circular spring is transferred to the tension ribbon and to the force balance by means of knife edges.

The insert of the multiplying relay is fixed to the base plate of a light metal housing through a plug-in connection for the nozzle air supply (Fig. 125).

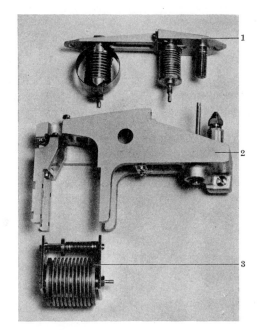

1 Pneumatic Force Balance with
  Bellows and Circular Spring System
2 Tension Device with Elastic Ribbon,
  Tension Lever, and Nozzle
3 Tension Bellows with Zero Point Spring

Fig. 124   Components of the TELEPNEU Multiplying Relay Insert.

Fig. 125   TELEPNEU Multiplying Relay, Cover Removed.

1 Multiplying Relay
2 Amplifier
3 Connections to Control Station
4 Housing
5 "O" Rings

The pneumatic amplifier and the input restrictor (Fig. 120) are also screwed into the housing and can be easily exchanged. The air goes to the bellows through hoses. The required hose connection sockets are screwed into the housing and into the insert of the multiplying relay.

4. TYPES AND MOUNTING

For the various applications in ratio and cascade controls, the multiplying relay is coupled either with the standard or the ex-

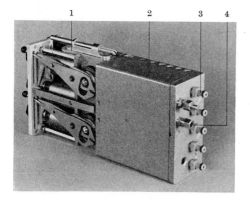

1 Expanded Control Station
2 Multiplying Relay
3 Plug-In Connections to Controller Base Plate
4 Compressed Air Connections (Ermeto)

Fig. 126

Complete Unit Incorporating Multiplying Relay and Expanded Control Station.

panded control station (Fig. 126). Therefore, the air connections on the multiplying relay housing have to be adapted to the required type of control station. There is, however, only one type of insert for the multiplying relay as shown in Fig. 123. Corresponding to its application in ratio or cascade control, the insert is merely calibrated for different zero points (Figs. 121 and 122). The different types of the multiplying relay differ by the housing connections and by the internal switching facilities.

Fig. 127 shows the circuit and the external air connections of the most frequently used type of the multiplying relay. It is used in ratio and cascade controls, where the pressure ratio is adjusted in the expanded control station (Type "a") and where a bumpless transfer to fixed set point control of the slave variable is possible.

Connections to Controller and Plant

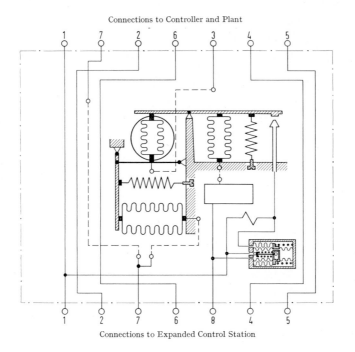

Connections to Expanded Control Station

Meaning of Connections:

1—1 Air Supply
2—2 Through Connecting Hole
3   Inlet (Measured Value of the Non-controlled Variable) with Ratio Control or
      Outlet Pressure of the Master Controller with Cascade Control
4—4)
5—5) } Through Connecting Holes
6—6)
7—7 Ratio Setting Pressure
8   Outlet (Set Point of the Controller)

Fig. 127   External Connections and Internal Circuit of the Multiplying Relay
           Combined with the Expanded Control Station.

The air connections are numbered with the same figures as in the
circuit diagrams of the combined Teleperm-Telepneu System.
For the multiplying relay in cascade ratio control, the ratio adjusting pressure comes from the master controller through connection 7.
In this case, contrary to the circuit diagram in Fig. 127, lower connection 7 has no pressure.
Before mounting in the panel board, the expanded control stations
and multiplying relay are firmly screwed together. In this way, the

Connections to Controller and Plant

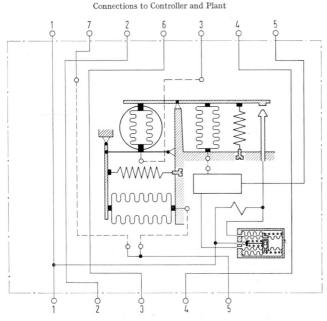

Connections to the Standard Control Station

Meaning of Connections:

1—1   Air Supply
2—2
3—6 } Through Connecting Holes
4—4
3   Input (Measured Value of the Non-controlled Variable) with Ratio Control or
        Output Pressure of the Master Controller with Cascade Control
5 and 7 Ratio Setting Pressure

Fig. 128   External Connections and Internal Circuit of the Multiplying Relay
            Combined with the Standard Control Station.

air connections are sealed with "O" ring washers which have been installed in the multiplying relay (Fig. 125).

At most, five air connections are needed for coupling the multiplying relay with a standard control station. These are always plastic plug-in connectors which are screwed into the control station. Similar to the expanded type, the standard control station is firmly screwed together with the multiplying relay, forming a complete unit corresponding to Fig. 126. For mounting in the panel board, bearing plates and screws are used and are tightened against the panel board.

Fig. 128 shows the circuit diagram and the connection legend for the combination of the multiplying relay with the standard control station.

A different type is designed for cascade ratio control; by changing the hose arrangement, connection 5 to the control station (Type "b") receives no pressure.

If plug-in controllers (Fig. 129) are used, the connections to the controller shown in Figs. 127 and 128 are plastic plug-in connectors

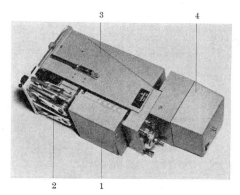

1 Multiplying Relay
2 Expanded Control Station
3 Pneumatic Recorder
4 Pneumatic Plug-In Controller

Fig. 129
TELEPNEU Multiplying Relay on a Pneumatic Recorder with Plug-In Controller and Expanded Control Station.

which are screwed into the multiplying relay and go pressure-tight into the controller connecting panel.

If the multiplying relay is to work together with controllers situated in the plant, it is equipped with the appropriate Ermeto compression fittings to connect the tubing.

5. Adjustment and Testing

If a multiplying relay is to be used for ratio control with a manually adjusted ratio, the zero point is to be checked before starting the operation. When the uncontrolled variable has the measured pressure of 0.2 kg/cm², the set point value for the controlled variable must also be 0.2 kg/cm² for any adjusted pressure ratio. If necessary, the zero point spring must be slightly readjusted. It is accessible from the outside through an opening in the housing.

As the device is very dependable, disturbances during operation are hardly to be expected. In spite of this, should errors still occur they can come only from contamination of the input restrictor, of the amplifier or of the nozzle if a heavily contaminated supply air has gotten into the instrument.

If incorrect operation is suspected, the multiplying relay must be disassembled. For testing and recalibrating, the circuit shown in Fig. 120 is set up. The input restrictor must have a bore of 0.3 mm and a length of 10 mm. In addition, three sensitive pressure gauges are needed for indicating the three pressures and, further, two precision pressure transmitters for the two input pressures.

If the instrument has been calibrated for ratio control, both input pressures are adjusted to 0.2 kg/cm², the output pressure must also be 0.2 kg/cm², and zero point spring 2 has to be readjusted if necessary. If the input pressure 2 is increased to 1.0 kg/cm², the output pressure must not vary. If necessary, the nozzle must be turned and spring 2 readjusted. Then, input pressure 1 must be adjusted to 0.6 kg/cm². With input pressure 2 equalling 0.2 kg/cm², the output pressure must be 0.4 kg/cm² and, with the former equalling 1.0 kg/cm², the latter must also be 1.0 kg/cm². If this is not the case, the compensating bellows and the tension in zero point spring 1 have to be readjusted. Here, care must be taken that after any adjustment of the compensating bellows the zero point of the output pressure has to be again readjusted by changing the tension in zero point spring 2.

If the relay has been calibrated for cascade control, both input pressures are adjusted to 0.6 kg/cm², the output pressure must also equal 0.6 kp/cm² and, if necessary, zero point spring 2 is again readjusted. Here, too, the output pressure must not vary when input pressure 2 is varied in the range from 0.2 to 1.0 kg/cm². If necessary, the nozzle must be turned and spring 2 readjusted. Then, input pressure 1 will increase to 0.8 kg/cm². If input pressure 2 equals 0.2 kg/cm², the output pressure must equal 0.7 kg/cm². If input pressure 2 equals 1.0 kg/cm², the output pressure must equal 1.0 kg/cm². If this is not the case, the position of the compensating bellows and the tension of the zero balance spring 1 again have to be readjusted. Here, also, the zero point of the output pressure must be readjusted by adjustment of spring 2 after any adjustment of the bellows.

6. TECHNICAL DATA

Bore of nozzle	1.0 mm dia.
Bore of input restrictor	0.3 mm dia.
Flapper travel to the nozzle for full actuating range of the nozzle-flapper system	0.003 mm
Pneumatically adjustable pressure ratio range	1 : 2 to 2 : 1
Zero shift for change of the ratio from 0.5 to 2.	0.3% maximum
Zero point change for a variation in supply air pressure by 1/10 kg/cm² in the range of 1.2 to 1.6 kg/cm²	0.5% maximum
Zero point change for a variation in temperature by 10ºC in the range from +20 to +60ºC	0.2%
Air consumption	4 Std. l/min
Maximum output air flow	$\geq$ 50 Std. l/min

IV. ELECTROPNEUMATIC INSTRUMENTS

A. The Transition from Pneumatic to Electropneumatic

In a combined control system the gaps between electric and pneumatic controls are bridged by electropneumatic instruments. These must offer the possibility of changing from one type of utility to the other anywhere in the control loop. Only thus, it is feasible to really comprehensively plan and instrument according to control and process aspects.

The TELEPERM-TELEPNEU System technique bridges this gap very simply and completely. The pneumatic force balance devices are so designed as to allow expansion to the respective electropneumatic instrument by merely attaching a moving coil system.

1. THE ELECTROPNEUMATIC FORCE BALANCE

The pneumatic force balance is expanded into the electropneumatic force balance by assembly with the moving coil system (Fig. 130).

Fig. 130
Moving Coil System, Plastic
Cover Removed.

The moving coil system is so dimensioned that the force effect introduces a torque on the balance beam that corresponds to the torque of one of the inner bellows. Thus, it is possible to replace a pneumatic input signal on the force balance by an electric one and, thereby, to change from a pure pneumatic to an electropneumatic force balance. The electric input signal is compensated pneumatically by means of bellows or mechanically by means of a helical spring, according to the respective type of device. Thus, the pneumatic devices give rise to the line of the electropneumatic controllers, transducers, and positioners.

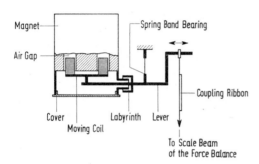

Fig. 131

Schematic Cross Section of the Moving Coil System.

2. The Moving Coil System

a) Principle and Operation

The moving coil system consists of a pot-shaped magnet in whose circular air gap is a moving coil (Fig. 131). If a direct current flows through the moving coil, the latter tends to move up or down in the magnetic field of the magnet according to the direction of the current. This motion of the moving coil is transmitted by a two-armed lever and a coupling ribbon to the force balance and is limited by it to some thousandths of a millimeter. The balance beam of the force balance thus receives a torque, the amount and direction of which is proportional to the current in the moving coil. To balance this torque, the linkage of the coupling ribbon on the lever of the moving coil can be changed. The winding of the moving coil is suitable for a current range of 50 ma, making it compatible with the standardized electric system.

b) Construction

The preadjusted moving coil system is mounted on the force balance. The final precise adjustment is done together with the force balance.

The moving coil system is considered explosion-proof, if the electric device connected in series meets the explosion-proof specifications and the input current in no case exceeds 100 ma. The coiled winding is isolated in a molded aluminum capsule (Fig. 132). The lever affected by the moving coil rests on spring bands. To avoid the

Fig. 132
The Metal-Cladded Moving Coil.

infiltration of iron chips into the magnet gap, the lever goes through a labyrinth out of the chamber enclosing the air gap and the moving coil (Fig. 131). The chamber itself is sealed with a plastic cover (Fig. 130).

c) Adjustment

The final fine adjustment of the electropneumatic force balance — like that of the pneumatic force balance — is done by merely shifting the bellows. Therefore, pre-adjustment of the moving coil system is necessary. The pivot point of the coupling ribbon is moved until a current of 50 ma produces a force of 550 g on the coupling ribbon.

3. Types of Electropneumatic Force Balances

For the TELEPERM-TELEPNEU instruments, five different designs of electropneumatic force balances are used (Fig. 133):

a) The Electropneumatic Five-Bellows Force Balance

The electropneumatic five-bellows force balance is used in electropneumatic proportional-plus-reset action and in proportional-plus-
reset-plus-rate action plug-in controllers. It forms the deviation
by balancing the torque of the moving coil with that of one of the inner
bellows. The two external bellows (feedback bellows) act the same
way as in the pneumatic five-bellows force balance.

b) The Electropneumatic Four-Bellows Force Balance

The four-bellows force balance is used in electropneumatic flow
controllers. It differs from the five-bellows force balance with
moving coil only in another type of feedback that again corresponds
to that of the pneumatic four-bellows force balance.

c) The Electropneumatic Two-Bellows Force Balance

This instrument is used in electropneumatic single-acting positioners.
It corresponds to the pneumatic three-bellows force balance,
except that here the control bellows is replaced by the moving coil.

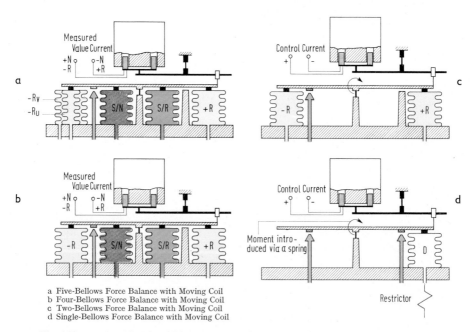

a Five-Bellows Force Balance with Moving Coil
b Four-Bellows Force Balance with Moving Coil
c Two-Bellows Force Balance with Moving Coil
d Single-Bellows Force Balance with Moving Coil

Fig. 133 a to d.   Models of Electropneumatic Force Balances.

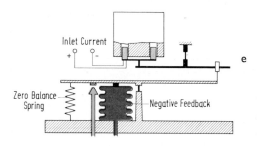

Fig. 133e

Models of the Electropneumatic Single-Bellows Force Balance with Moving Coil and Zero Balance Spring.

d) *The Electropneumatic Single-Bellows Force Balance*

This force balance serves as a balancing element in double-acting positioners, corresponding to the pneumatic two-bellows force balance.

e) *The Electropneumatic Single-Bellows Force Balance with Zero Balance Spring*

This force balance is the electropneumatic balancing system of the TELEPERM-TELEPNEU transducer. The zero point is preadjusted to 0.2 kg/cm² by the adjustable zero balance spring. The inner bellows constitutes the degenerative feedback of the moving coil.

4. MOUNTING OF THE MOVING COIL SYSTEM

The moving coil system is fastened by four screws to the pneumatic force balance (Fig. 134). The coupling ribbon is connected to the force balance by a clamp. Before fastening the coupling ribbon, the moving coil is pressed against the core of the magnet and then raised by about 1 mm. If the coupling band is clamped in this position, the moving coil is located in the correct place within the homogeneous field of the magnet.

5. ADJUSTMENT AND TESTING

The electropneumatic force balances are furnished as adjusted units. They can be interchanged in the plant without requiring readjustment of the instruments. If, in exceptional cases, it is mandatory to interchange damaged components, the following checking and adjustment has to be done very carefully so that the instrument works again with its usual accuracy after repairing the force balance.

For the testing and adjustment, a d-c generator is needed with a continuous current adjustment from 0 to 60 ma and an accuracy of 0.2%.

Testing and adjustment are to be carried out as described below:

a) The Force Balances of the Electropneumatic Controllers

As the electropneumatic force balances of the controllers are assembled from the preadjusted moving coil system and a tested

Fig. 134
The Electropneumatic Force Balance.

and adjusted pneumatic force balance, the testing is limited to the following points. The test circuit is shown in Fig. 135.

In spite of the increased pneumatic amplification, a compensating circuit is used to make possible a more accurate and dependable balancing of the electropneumatic force balance.

Balancing the inner bellows

The pivot point of the coupling ribbon on the lever of the moving coil system is adjusted in such a way that a current variation of 50 ma corresponds to a pressure change of 0.8 kg/cm^2 in the inner bellows. The balancing technique used in the compensating circuitry assumes consideration of the actuating range of the system. In doing so, the actuating range is determined by the pressure difference $p_{e_1} - p_{e_2}$ of the inner bellows which, at the end of the open system, creates a pressure change of 0.8 kg/cm² in p_a. In the test circuit (Fig. 135), both switches are shown in the required position 1.

For the adjustment, a variable direct current is put on the moving coil and, with no pressure in the feedback bellows, the amplifier output pressure is switched to the inner bellows on the nozzle side. The moving coil must be so poled that it operates against these

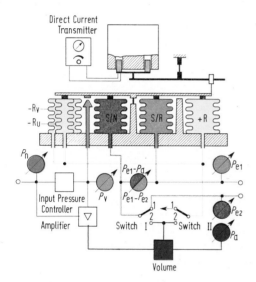

Fig. 135

Force Balance with Moving Coil Five-Bellows Testing and Adjusting Circuit.

bellows. The balancing occurs in such a way that, with a variation in moving coil current from 12.5 to 50 ma, the amplifier output pressure goes through a pressure range from 0.2 to 0.8 kg/cm² minus the measured actuating range:

> With switch I in position 2, switch II in position 1, p_{e_1} switched off and bled off, adjust moving coil current to 12.5 ma; adjust nozzle so that the amplifier output pressure equals 0.2 kg/cm²; increase moving coil current to 50 ma; the amplifier output pressure must now equal 0.8 kg/cm² minus the measured actuating range. This can be achieved by varying the pivot point of the coupling ribbon on the lever of the moving coil system.

> After each move, the nozzle must be readjusted so that a moving coil current of 12.5 ma again corresponds to an amplifier output pressure of 0.2 kg/cm².

Balancing the external bellows

The external bellows are balanced in such a way that the force balance, with feedback fully switched-on, is in unstable balance for all output pressures of the amplifier. This is the case if the actuating range is just compensated by a regenerative feedback:

> With switch I and switch II in position 2, p_{e_1} switched off and bled off; adjust moving coil current to 12.5 ma; adjust nozzle so that the amplifier output pressure equals 0.2 kg/cm²; increase moving coil current to 50 ma; by turning the eccentric, so adjust those external bellows not covered by the moving coil system, that the amplifier output pressure exactly equals 0.8 kg/cm².
>
> After each adjustment of the eccentric, the nozzle has to be so readjusted that, with a moving coil current of 12.5 ma, the amplifier output pressure is again 0.2 kg/cm².

b) The Force Balance of the Electropneumatic Transducer

In this electropneumatic force balance, an input current in the range of 0 to 50 ma must produce an output pressure from 0.2 to 1.0 kg/cm². Testing and adjustment of the force balance are always done in the instrument itself, so that a special test circuit is superfluous.

Balancing is again accomplished by shifting the coupling ribbon on the transmission lever of the moving coil system. The output pressure of 0.2 kg/cm² with no current in the moving coil is obtained by corresponding initial stress of the zero balance spring. Because adjustment of the range can change the tension in the spring, the zero point must be checked and, if necessary, readjusted after each adjustment of the lever arm.

c) The Force Balances of the Electropneumatic Positioners

The force balances of the electropneumatic positioners are calibrated only together with the positioning motors. The feedback bellows in single-acting positioners are adjusted like the pneumatic ones.

6. TECHNICAL DATA

Length . . . . 92 mm

Width . . . . 52 mm

Height . . . . 55 mm

Weight . . . . 0.5 kg

Resistance of the moving coil . . . . . 145 ohms $\pm 10\%$

Maximum overloading of the moving coil
for several hours . . . . up to 150 ma

Air gap induction of the magnet . . . . 3500 gauss

Actuating range of the electropneumatic
force balances, according to type . . 0.2 to 0.5%

B. The Electropneumatic Instruments

The pneumatic devices of the TELEPNEU system become electro-pneumatic devices merely by exchanging the pneumatic components with their counterparts in the electropneumatic force balances. Aside from performing their usual functions of measuring, amplifying, and controlling, the resulting electropneumatic instruments also perform the additional function of converting from electric to pneumatic. Parallel to the line of pneumatic force balance devices is the corresponding line of electropneumatic instruments.
These are:
The proportional-plus-reset action and the proportional-plus-reset-plus-rate action controllers for panel board and local mounting, flow controllers, and positioners for the different types of pneumatic diaphragm motors. In addition, there is a new device; the electro-pneumatic transducer. Its place is where purely pneumatic control has to be extended to variables arising from electric measurements. The essential advantage of this special kind of transition to electro-pneumatics is that it offers the operator a completely standardized technique. The result is that the various pneumatic or electro-pneumatic instruments do not differ basically with regard to their external appearance, their handling, their operation, and their installation. All instruments contain components of the TELEPNEU

System so that the amplification and the formation of the transient behavior are always performed by approved pneumatic means.

1. THE ELECTROPNEUMATIC CONTROLLERS

a) Special Features

In all electropneumatic controllers, an electric actual value is compared with a pneumatic set point value. Consequently, these

1 Electric Recorder   3 Electropneumatic Controller
2 Pneumatic Control Station   4 Pneumatic Set Point Indicator

Fig. 136   Electropneumatic Control Unit.

controllers can always be combined with an electric recording or indicating instrument for the actual value and with a pneumatic set point value indicator. A pneumatic instrument in the TELEPNEU System is used here as a control station (Fig. 136).

The proportional-plus-reset action and the proportional-plus-reset-plus-rate action controllers for control rooms are mounted on the rear of electric recorders. For plant installation they are provided with a short circuit relay exactly like the flow controllers.

In their static and dynamic qualities, the electropneumatic controllers do not differ from the pneumatic ones. The pneumatic circuits are also identical. This is seen by comparing the circuit diagram of the proportional-plus-reset-plus-rate action controller or flow controller (Figs. 137 and 138) with the corresponding TELEPNEU controllers.

According to the controller action (direct or indirect), the moving coil system replaces either one of the inner bellows of the force balance. The control deviation is formed by the resulting torque of the moving coil and one of the inner bellows.

With a direct acting controller, the set point pressure goes to the inner bellows on the nozzle side of the force balance; the other inner bellows remain closed and are bled off (Fig. 137). When the controller action is reversed to indirect, the set point pressure goes to these bellows. The moving coil is poled in such a way that it acts against the torque of the set point bellows. A measured value current of 0 to 50 ma corresponds to a set point pressure of 0 to $0.8 \, kg/cm^2$. This current supplied by the transmitter has been preadjusted so that it is, to a large extent, independent of the resistance. Therefore, resistance changes in the moving coil due to heating have just as little influence on the measurement and control accuracy as variations in line resistance.

b) Construction

The electropneumatic controller series is shown in Fig. 139.

The moving coil of the controllers is connected in series with the recording and indicating devices. The electrical connections of the force balance with the moving coil are marked P (positive) and N (negative). If the controller is direct acting, the positive pole of the transmitter output goes to P and the negative pole to N. For indirect acting controllers, the moving coil polarity is reversed.

The controller air connections are the same as for the pneumatic instruments. For a panel board controller, the unneeded connecting plugs to the pneumatic recorder are closed. The connection of the pneumatic measured value (connection 3) remains open in order to vent the free inner bellows that has been replaced by the moving coil.

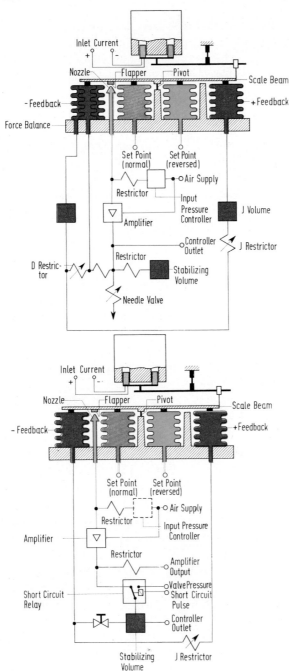

Fig. 137
Electropneumatic
PID Controller Circuit.

Fig. 138
Electropneumatic Flow
Controller Circuit.

a. TELEPERM-TELEPNEU PID Controller
b. TELEPERM-TELEPNEU PI Controller
c. TELEPERM-TELEPNEU Flow Controller

Fig. 139   The Line of Electropneumatic Controllers.

c) Testing of the Controllers

The electropneumatic controllers are devices in which an electric variable is compared with a pneumatic one. Therefore, their function can no longer be checked by a simple differential pressure gauge as in the TELEPNEU standardized controllers. Here, current and pressure must be compared by separate instruments whose absolute measuring accuracy must correspond to the precision of the controllers. For the rest, testing the electropneumatic controllers follows the same aspects as for the pneumatic ones. The tightness of all connector plugs and the control accuracy over the whole control range are both tested. The test circuits used are also basically the same, the controller output pressure being fed to the input as a degenerative feedback.

The test circuits for proportional-plus-reset action and proportional-plus-reset-plus-rate action controllers, as well as for flow controllers, are shown in Figs. 140 and 141.

The plug-in controllers are suitably tested as a unit, together with the electric recorder and the pneumatic control station the controller action being reversed (position "R" of the switch). The control station switch is put in "AUTOMATIC" and the set point pressure transmitter is adjusted to zero. Besides, the set point

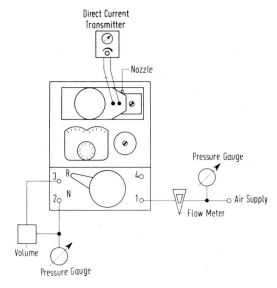

Fig. 140

Electropneumatic PI (PID)
Controller Test Circuit.

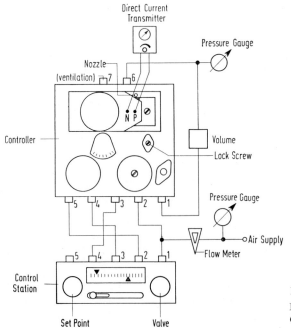

Fig. 141

Electropneumatic Flow
Controller Test Circuit.

connection in the controller (connection 4) must be open so that the set point bellows has no pressure and does not create a torque disturbing the force balance. For the flow controller, a control station must also be used so that the function of the short circuit relay can be tested as well.

Testing for tightness:

With a supply pressure of 1.4 kg/cm² and an input current of 50 ma, the air consumption must not exceed 9 Std. l/min.

Zero point adjustment:

With the moving coil current being 25 ma, the controller output pressure is adjusted to 0.4 kg/cm² by turning the nozzle on the force balance. Contrary to the pneumatic transmitters, the electric ones operate without life zero so that the range for a set point pressure of 0.8 kg/cm² also has to begin with zero.

Testing the accuracy of control:

The accuracy of control is determined by the balancing of the force balance. Thus, in the electropneumatic controllers, too, the zero stability during variations in load is fixed only by the amplification and by the adjustment of the feedback bellows. Therefore, supplementary adjustment of the complete controller is unnecessary except for zero point correction. Therefore, the testing can be limited to checking the function. This is effected by fixing an output pressure range from 0.08 to 0.8 kg/cm² to a current from 5 to 50 ma.

Testing the short circuit set:

With the control station switch in the "MANUAL" position, the pressure of the valve pressure transmitter must go to the controller output. To be tested is whether identical pressures are indicated by the lower pointer of the double pressure gauge and on the controller output pressure gauge.

d) Putting Into Operation and Tuning to the Controlled System

Identical technique in electropneumatic and pneumatic controllers has already been emphasized as an essential principle of the TELEPERM-TELEPNEU System. It is decisive for the operator that the handling and start-up of all instruments, even in combined pneumatic and electropneumatic plants, are completely similar. So, especially for the adaptation of electropneumatic controllers to the controlled system, the pneumatic technique methods particularly apply.

e) Technical Data

Proportional-plus-reset action and proportional-plus-reset-plus-rate action controllers:

Dimensions . . . . 185 mm × 206 mm × 166 mm
Weight . . . . 5.8 kg
Adjustable proportional band range 10 to 300%
Supply pressure error with input
   pressure controller . . . . . . $\dfrac{0.2\% \text{ sustained deviation}}{0.1 \text{ kg/cm}^2 \text{ supply pressure variation}}$

Supply pressure error without input
   pressure controller in the range
   from 1.1 to 1.6 kg/cm². . . . . $\dfrac{0.5\% \text{ sustained deviation}}{0.1 \text{ kg/cm}^2 \text{ supply pressure variation}}$

Adjustable reset time . . . . . . 0.1 to 30 min
Adjustable rate time . . . . . . 0.05 to 15 min
Actuating range . . . . 0.6% maximum
Zero point change by varying the
   proportional band range . . . . 0.5% maximum
Sustained control deviation with
   proportional band range of 300% 0.2%
Sensitivity 0.01%
Measured value input . . . . . . 0 to 50 ma, 145 ohms
Set point input . . . . 0 to 0.8 kg/cm²
Average air consumption . . . . 5 Std. l/min
Maximum output air flow . . . . ≧ 50 Std. l/min

Flow controllers:

Dimensions . . . . 180 mm × 162 mm × 148 mm
Weight . . . . 3.8 kg
Adjustable reset time . . . . . . 2 to 600 sec

Actuating range . . . . 0.5% maximum
Sustained deviation 0.2%
Sensitivity 0.01%
Supply pressure error without input
   pressure controller . . . . . . $\dfrac{0.1\% \text{ sustained deviation}}{0.1 \text{ kg/cm}^2 \text{ supply pressure variation}}$

Measured value input . . . . . . 0 to 50 ma, 145 ohms
Set point input . . . . 0 to 0.8 kg/cm²
Average air consumption with no
   load . . . . 5 Std. l/min
Maximum output air flow . . . . $\geq$ 50 Std. l/min

2. THE ELECTROPNEUMATIC POSITIONERS

a) The Expansion of the Pneumatic to Electropneumatic Positioners

The combination of electric controllers with pneumatic positioners requires the transducing of electric signals into pneumatic ones. It is obvious that to combine this operation with a position control means using electropneumatic positioners. The electropneumatic positioners are derived from the corresponding pneumatic positioners by adding the moving coil system.

These electropneumatic positioners receive as an input variable a preadjusted direct current which is supplied either from an electric controller or from manual actuation. The electric positioning signal is compared with the position of the diaphragm motor at the balance beam of the electropneumatic force balance.

With this expansion of the force balance by the moving coil system there results from the series of pneumatic positioners the corresponding series of the electropneumatic ones (Fig. 142). Similar to the corresponding pneumatic devices, Type "a" is designed for spring-balanced diaphragm motors and Type "b" for double-acting springless motors. Type "c" is designed as a power positioner for high positioning speeds.

The pneumatic and electropneumatic positioners differ only in that the master variable for the position control is, in one case, pneumatic, and in the other, electric. The closed loop of the position control is,

Fig. 142   The Line of Electropneumatic Positioners.

consequently, the same in both cases because the master variables are externally imposed, thereby not influencing the dynamic behavior of the control. The result is a complete mutualness of the pneumatic and electropneumatic positioners with respect to their function, their construction, their application, their installation, adjustment, and start-up. It is, therefore, needless to discuss these details again.

b) Special Features

The functional uniformity of all positioners requires an electric positioning signal range from 10 to 60 ma, corresponding to the command pressure range from 0.2 to 1.0 kg/cm² of the pneumatic positioners.

The electropneumatic positioners convert an electric positioning signal into a pneumatic variable. Therefore, unlike the pneumatic positioner, the positioning signal cannot be switched directly to the positioning motor. Consequently, the electropneumatic positioners have no switch-off arrangements.

c) Technical Data

Length . . . . ⎫
Width . . . . ⎪
Height . . . . ⎬ Same as the pneumatic positioners
Weight . . . . ⎭

Standard supply pressure . . . . 1.4 kg/cm²
Maximum supply pressure . . . . 2.0 kg/cm²
Actuating current range . . . . 10 to 60 ma
Input resistance . . . . 145 ohms
Continuously adjustable travel range . . . . 20 to 75 mm
Linearity error 0.5%
Hysteresis 0.5%
Actuating range 0.5%
Sensitivity 0.01%
Supply pressure error . . . . . 0.2% position deviation
──────────────────
0.1 kg/cm² supply pressure
variation

Average air consumption:

Single-acting positioner . . . . 5 Std. l/min
Double-acting positioner . . . . 10 Std. l/min
Power positioner . . . . 10 Std. l/min

Maximum output air flow:

Single-acting positioner . . . . ≥ 50 Std. l/min
Double-acting positioner . . . . ≥ 50 Std. l/min
Power positioner . . . . ≥100 Std. l/min

3. The Electropneumatic Transducer

In addition to the instruments performing the combined functions of transmitting and controlling—for example, the electropneumatic controllers and positioners—devices are needed which are designed only for transducing. This is the case where, in all-pneumatic instrumented plants, individual variables must be handled electrically. The transducer is then installed between the electric transmitter and the pneumatic controller. This requires very high transmission accuracy and good dynamic behavior.

a) Mode of Operation

The TELEPERM-TELEPNEU transducer operates according to the force balance principle with pneumatic compensation of the electric input variable.

The forces exerted on the balance beam of the electropneumatic force balance (Fig. 143) by the moving coil, the compensating bellows, and the zero balance spring all create a resulting torque around the pivot. If the pressure in the compensating bellows does not correspond to the current in the moving coil, the output pressure is varied over the nozzle and amplifier until balance is obtained. To avoid transmission errors caused by variations in supply pressure, the restrictor pressure to the nozzle is additionally controlled. For this purpose, the input pressure controller

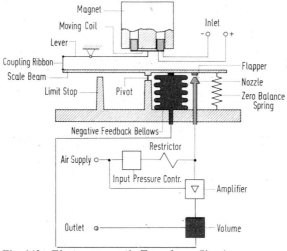

Fig. 143   Electropneumatic Transducer Circuit.

is used, which is the case in the controllers when especially high accuracy is needed. In order that the device produce a zero point pressure of 0.2 kg/cm² with no current in moving coil, the zero balance spring with an appropriate initial stress is applied to the force balance. A current change in the moving coil of 0 to 50 ma produces an amplifier output pressure change of 0.2 to 1.0 kg/cm², through which change the balance beam of the force balance turns only by about 3 or 4 thousandths of a millimeter because of the high sensitivity of the pneumatic amplifier system. The dynamic behavior of the electropneumatic transducer is similar to that of an element having two storages with extremely small delay time and time constant. As shown in Fig. 144, the transient behavior after a sudden variation in input current demonstrates that the device operates practically without delay.

The delay time T_u amounts to about 15 msec and the time constant T to about 50 msec.

b) Construction

The construction of the transducer is shown in Fig. 145.

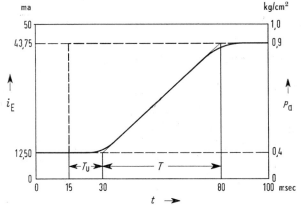

Fig. 144

Transient Behavior of the Transducer.

1 Base Plate
2 Input Pressure Controller
3 Connection Plate
4 Electropneumatic Force Balance
5 Amplifier

Fig. 145

TELEPERM-TELEPNEU Transducer.

The connecting plate forms one wall of the housing, carries the cover and contains the hole for the electric input cable as well as the pneumatic connections for the supply air and instrument output. The plug-in components go into the base plate that contains the pneumatic switch and the damping volume. The components are the electropneumatic force balance, the input pressure controller, and the pneumatic amplifier.

c) Operation

The transducer is a particularly simple and rugged device, assembled from tested and adjusted components like all others in the TELEPERM-TELEPNEU System. The instrument is calibrated for normal installation position where the force balance is vertical. If mounting in a different position is necessary, the zero point must be slightly adjusted by turning the nozzle on the force balance. The zero point is fixed so that, with no current in the moving coil, the output pressure must be 0.2 kg/cm².

The functioning of the transducer is easily checked. For that purpose, an adjustable current is put in and the output pressure is measured with an accurate pressure gauge. With this simple arrangement all technical data such as range, linearity, and hysteresis can be checked.

d) Technical Data

Length . . . . ⎫	
Width . . . . ⎬ Same as the TELEPNEU positioners	
Height . . . . ⎪	
Weight . . . . ⎭	
Input . . . . 0 to 50 ma, 145 ohms	
Output . . . . 0.2 to 1.0 kg/cm²	
Air supply pressure . . . . 1.4 kg/cm²	
Measuring accuracy 0.5%	
Actuating range 0.5%	
Linearity error 0.1%	
Hysteresis . . . . < 0.05%	
Supply pressure error in the range from	
1.1 to 1.6 kg/cm² per 0.1 kg/cm²	
supply pressure variation 0.1%	

Temperature error . . . . 0.5%/30°C
Air consumption . . . . 5 Std. l/min
Maximum output air flow . . . . . ≧ 50 Std. l/min

C. Electric Standard Recorders

In the electropneumatic combination system, electric miniature recorders are needed in addition to the pneumatic ones. Quite frequently both kinds of recorders are installed side by side in the same panel board. Therefore, it is desirable that their appearance should be similar to maintain the uniformity of instrumentation and the outer appearance of control rooms (Fig. 146).

The electric recorder line of the TELEPERM System meets these requirements. Moreover, where possible, the same components are used; for example, recording unit, drive motor, and ink duct. In this way the maintenance of both devices is similar.

1. THE COMPONENTS

a) *The Measuring Element*

Single and double recorders contain the same measuring elements. They are so dimensioned that both measuring elements may be assembled side by side in the double recorder.

1 Pneumatic Recorder   2 Electric Recorder

Fig. 146 Pneumatic and Electric Recorders, Showing Uniform External Appearances.

The moving coil system has been constructed with an inner magnet so that the mutual influence and the influence of external fields are practically zero (Fig. 147).

An iron ring-shaped magnetic return path piece concentrically encloses the inner magnet and, together with it, establishes the circular air gap. The thick soft iron pole pieces create a homogeneous air gap induction over the whole extent of the air gap, whereby good linearity over the whole scale is obtained.

Firmly connected with the return path piece is the measuring system plate equipped with an eddy current or an oil damping according to the requirements.

The movable element has a light metal winding holder. In addition to the winding, it also has the armatures for spring locations and lead-in wires, the damping vane, the equalizer weights, and the connecting rod location.

Like all moving coil systems, the measuring element range is determined by the torque springs and by the turns of the moving coil. Apart from the 50-ma standard type, there are types for measuring ranges from 0.25 to 250 ma.

b) The Eddy Current Damping

A disc-like aluminum damping vane is firmly connected to the moving coil frame and, therefore, makes a rotation around the axle of the measuring element which corresponds to the deflection of the movable element (Fig. 147). In doing, so it moves in the air gap of a powerful magnet. Thus, an emf is created in the part of the damping disc situated beneath the pole surface, which again creates a current. This current, together with the field, establishes a torque opposing the movement and, thereby, restraining the motion.

With this damping device, damping factors can be obtained up to $\alpha = 1.6$ with a response time of 0.9 sec.

c) The Oil Damping

When damping factors are required where $\alpha > 1.6$, eddy current damping is replaced by oil damping. It consists of a silicon-oil-filled cylindrical container in which a vane is moved. The drive power is supplied from a gear whose teeth mate with the measuring element damping vane. With this oil damping, response times from a few seconds up to about 30 seconds can be obtained.

d) The Guide

The pointer of a measuring element usually describes an arc of a circle. Rectilinear coordinates are preferred because they provide

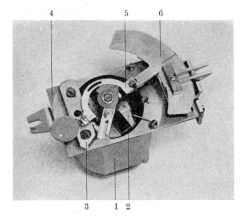

1 Ring-shaped Magnetic Return Path Piece
2 Magnet
3 Measuring Element Holder
4 Measuring System Plate
5 Movable Element
6 Damping Vane

Fig. 147

The Moving Coil Measuring Element of the Electric Recorder.

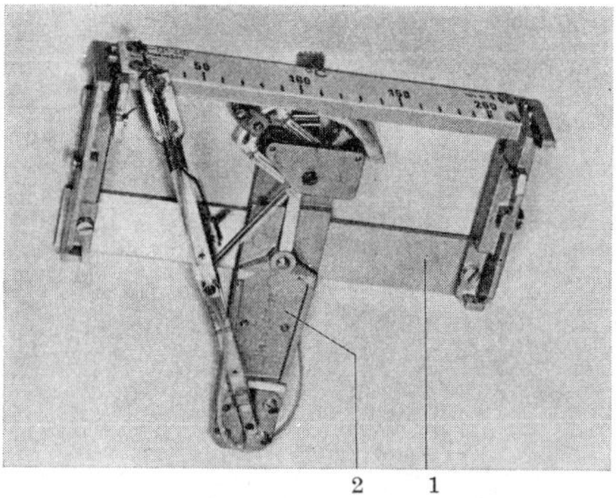

1 Scale Holder
2 Elliptical Guide

Fig. 148

Scale Holder with Elliptical Guide.

better clearness and analysis. The conversion of angular deflection into rectilinear motion is through the elliptical guide (Fig. 148).
This guide is an independent component fixed to the scale holder. Measuring element and guide rod are coupled through a connecting rod having jewelled bearings.
Aside from its robustness, the connecting rod elliptical guide has

the following advantages: the driving mechanism can be placed immediately behind the recording table. Consequently, the transmission to the paper feed cog wheels is very short. The heavy measuring elements can be placed firmly and accessibly in the recorder chassis.

The deviation of the calibration points from the strictly linear division is $< \pm 1.5\%$ of full scale range with a recording width of 100 mm; with a recording width of 45 mm, this deviation is $< \pm 0.8\%$.

e) Recording Unit and Drive Motor

The electric recorder has the same recording unit as the pneumatic recorder. See the description for the pneumatic recorder.

f) Writing Device and Ink Duct

At a cursory glance, the basic construction of the writing device in the electric recorder seems to be completely identical with that in the pneumatic recorder. Basically, it also consists of the ink container, the ink tube, the recording pen with capillary, and the air line (Fig. 149).

1 Chassis
2 Recording Unit
3 Motor
4 Zero Adjustment
5 Lifter for Pen
6 Air Tube for Squeeze Bulb
7 Lever for Recording Unit

Fig. 149   The Complete Chassis of the Electric Line Recorder.

1 Connecting
Terminals

2 Ground Screw

Fig. 150
Side View of the
Electric Recorder.

However, because the active torque available in the electric recorder is by an order of magnitude smaller than in the pneumatic recorder, the ink tube must be very flexible so that it creates only a negligibly small disturbance.

The writing pressure of the recording pen can be accurately adjusted with an adjusting weight.

2. CONSTRUCTION AND MOUNTING

All components of the electric recorder are mounted in a chassis, pushed into the housing, and screwed together with the latter. Measuring lines and current leads for the chart drive motor are connected to terminals at the left side of the recorder (Fig. 150). Right above this is a grounding screw. A wiring diagram is fastened on the outside of the housing.

The housing is dust- and spray water-proof and has a mounting depth of 290 mm. The TELEPERM-TELEPNEU controller can be plugged into the back panel.

The measuring elements have been isolated by plastic supports. They have been screwed into two crossbeams in the back half of the chassis by three screws each and can be brought to the right distance from the guide rod main axis by being shifted longitudinally. The scale holder with the guide rod arrangement is the end of the upper part of the front chassis. It can be easily removed after loosening the two screws. The lever for holding the recording unit is guided and locks into a hole on the right side of the scale holder. In the same way, the lever stop for the recording pen is located on the left side. The receptacle for the ink container is screwed in the right-hand side plate. Its height is adjustable.

For cleaning purposes, the recording pen can be removed from the front. In the two-pen recorder, both inking pens are supplied by one container.

Assembling the recording unit in the chassis is the same as for pneumatic recorders. Also, there are no differences in handling for loading chart paper or removing it.

Contrary to the pneumatic recorder, the housing is not injection molded, but is made of sheet metal. However, the mounting in the control panel is the same.

3. Types

There are two types: the single recorder with an effective chart paper width of 100 mm and the double recorder with an effective paper width of 45 mm each. Normally, both types are used with chart speeds of 20 and 60 mm/hr and a power supply of 220 volts, 50 cycles.

Special types result from variations in paper speed, chart motor voltage, and frequency.

4. Adjustment and Testing

By using the adjusting weight, the bearing pressure of the recording pen is so adjusted that, on the one hand, the paper friction is smaller than 0.5% and, on the other hand, readable diagrams can be recorded even with quick variations of the measuring values.

If not otherwise required, by adjusting the damping device a damping factor of $\alpha = 0.8$ is preset; that is, about 1.5% overshoot.

After eventual overloadings, a zero deviation may occur. This can be corrected again with the zero adjuster. The zero adjustment range extends over $\pm 5\%$ of the scale range.

5. START-UP AND MAINTENANCE

It has already been pointed out that with respect to their service the pneumatic and electric recorders hardly differ. This applies especially to loading the chart paper and removing the charts.

However, because of the essentially smaller torque of the electric recorder, the ink duct has to meet particularly high requirements. Above all, the ink level in the storage container always must be slightly higher than the opening of the recording capillary.

Putting it into operation is done as follows:

The recording unit is removed and the ink container is pulled out to the front. By using a pipette, the rear container is filled. After reassembly, the ink surface adjusts itself to a suitable level. The recording process is then initiated, as with the pneumatic recorder, by pressuring the ink container.

With longer intervals between operation, the recording capillary remains stationary on the chart paper and the ink dries up, blocking the capillary. To avoid this, the recording pen should be removed during such intervals, cleaned with water and then kept under water.

If the recording breaks down, the recording process can be started again by forcing air into the container (through the air tube by using a squeeze bulb). If this proves unsuccessful, the recording pen—especially the capillary—must be washed out with alcohol. Only seldom should it be necessary to wash out the complete ink line.

6. TECHNICAL DATA.

Measuring element current . . . . 50 ma
Power consumption . . . . 70 mw approx.
Friction error . . . . $< 0.5\%$ of the range
Linearity error . . . . $< +1.5\%$ of the range
Natural frequency . . . . 2.3 cps
Winding resistance . . . . 28 ohms approx.
Eddy current damping . . . . . . up to $\alpha = 1.6$
Oil damping . . . . up to $\alpha = 40$

INDEX